Beauty

COLLINS NUTSHELL BOOKS

Beauty

JOYCE McKINNELL

With Illustrations

COLLINS
LONDON AND GLASGOW

GENERAL EDITOR: J. B. FOREMAN, M.A.
First published 1964
This facsimile edition published 2009

Contents

© *William Collins Sons & Co. Ltd., 1964, 2009*
ISBN 978-0-00-729558-6
PRINTED IN HONG KONG
BY PRINTING EXPRESS LTD.

INTRODUCTION

Our menfolk may grin and say that we're mad when they catch glimpses of us at the hairdresser, or watch us creaming our faces, but we can continue our feminine ceremonies secure in the knowledge that we are following a long, long line of illustrious footsteps.

The early Egyptians, including Cleopatra, spent hours beautifying themselves with perfumes, almond oils, green eye paint and kohl eye black, and they fixed nard, an ointment made of lavender, to their hair. Poppaea, Nero's wife, lightened her skin with white lead and chalk, and many of the original Elizabethans used wine as a tonic water, splashing it on to their faces as we would a skin freshener. It is said that Mary Queen of Scots actually bathed in wine—one-upmanship on the milk bathers obviously!

In day-to-day life, the gentle, subtle pursuits of beauty should be among every woman's activities. But let's face it, once in a while we do tend to let ourselves go, and this is where *Blueprints for Beauty* steps in to nudge your elbow and say: "Come on! How about a fresh make-up, a different hair-style or a brand new beauty routine?"

Don't hide *Blueprints for Beauty* in a cupboard. Keep it on your dressing-table or by your bed as a personal reference book and an encouraging reminder that you can be beautiful, whatever your age.

However, before you turn the pages, maybe you should acquaint yourself with a bill that was introduced into Parliament in 1770, which said: "That all women of whatever age, rank, profession, or degree, whether virgins, maids, or widows, that shall, from and after such Act, impose upon, seduce, and betray into matrimony, any of

His Majesty's subjects, by the scents, paints, cosmetic washes, artificial teeth, false hair, Spanish wool, iron stays, hoops, high-heeled shoes, bolstered hips, shall incur the penalty of the law in force against witchcraft and like misdemeanours and that the marriage, upon conviction, shall stand null and void.''

To the best of my knowledge, this bill has never been rescinded.

You have been warned!

JOYCE MCKINNELL

Grateful acknowledgement is made to the following for their help and advice during the writing of this book: Lady Isobel Barnett; E. Hodges (Director) Garrard and Co. Ltd., Crown Jewellers; Cliff Michelmore; Lady Mavis Pilkington; Miss Molly Palmer; The Pearl Assurance Co. Ltd.; Miss E. M. Punchard (Secretary) Corset Guild of Great Britain; Edward Rayne, H. and M. Rayne Ltd., Shoemakers; Charles Revson (President) Revlon, New York; The Society of French Perfumers (Great Britain) Ltd.

1

FOCUS ON YOU

After a lecture once to a group of grey-haired over-forties, world famous beautician, Helena Rubinstein, told me: "Beauty is every woman's birthright."

This is absolutely true. It is possible for any woman to be beautiful in some way or another whether she is a plump outsize or a skinny lizzie with straight hair. You may not be all-over perfect, but who is? It is entirely up to you to make the best of what you have.

When she was younger Audrey Hepburn must have looked in her mirror, seen her thin figure, salt cellar collar-bones and bony arms, and thought: "Heavens, but I look so *plain!*" She could have left it at that, feeling more and more sorry for herself as the years advanced.

But she didn't. Instead, she really made the most of herself by accentuating her large eyes in order to remove attention from her figure, and wearing simple, perfectly groomed clothes that transformed her thinness from an obstacle into a blessing.

Today, Audrey Hepburn is regarded throughout the world as a chic and beautiful woman. You too, can be more attractive from today forward, if you are willing to give yourself a little more attention, a little more freshness, a little more fragrance, a little more grooming and much more action.

None of this need be considered time wasting. After all, you have to live with your face and figure for the rest of your life.

Make a start now. Strip down to your birthday suit and

have a look at yourself in the bedroom mirror. What kind of a person are you, figuratively speaking?

Are you tall, small, thin or plump? Whatever your height you can tell whether you have too much flesh for your own particular size (don't make the mistake of trying to look like a fashion model if you were born naturally short and plump) by pinching between your thumb and first finger the flesh on your midriff, stomach, hips and bottom. If you can hold more than an inch in any of these places it is a signal for diet, exercise or both!

Another way to discover if you are too fleshy around the thighs and bottom is to sit down, minus your girdle or corset, and see if you can pinch extra flesh at the sides. If you can, there is too much.

Interrogate yourself and answer honestly. Is your midriff on the bony side? Has your waist lost its shape? Are you round shouldered, is your bosom large, small or frankly droopy? Do you bulge around the tummy or are you thick around the ankles? Make a mental note of your findings, so that you can rectify matters with the appropriate advice later in this book.

Before you read further, however, do remember that every size of figure has its assets and advantages. Plumpness usually makes for a cheerful disposition, as handsome film star Rossano Brazzi knew only too well when he married his happy outsize wife. A thin woman is often blessed with great stores of mental and physical energy and she can wear clothes well.

Of course, it is one thing to discover your faults, and another thing entirely when it comes to improvement. Exercises, for instance, take time. What you need to give your morale an almost instant boost are some speedy beautifiers.

Here, then, is your plan. First of all, the *people* you should see.

Hairdresser

Visit a really good hairdresser, even if it n... going without some extra cigarettes or a few cinema v...ts. Let him re-style your hair completely. If you've had it tightly curled until now, try it sleek and smooth. If it is long, try it worn up, and if it is shorter, try it swept into a pretty artificial chignon at the back. Nothing works more wonders for your morale and beauty than a good session at the hairdresser.

Beauty Consultant

This is the girl behind the beauty counter in your local big store and her advice costs you nothing. Let her look at your skin and prescribe the correct colour of foundation, powder and lipstick. It is not impossible that you have been wearing the wrong shades to date. Also keep a watch for the visit of a consultant from one of the major cosmetic organisations. They often give individual demonstration make-ups for around ten shillings.

Manicurist and Chiropodist

The former may be at your hairdresser, and you can find the name of a qualified chiropodist from your doctor or local health department. Treatment from both these professionals will draw your own attention to hands and feet which may have been neglected, and will provide you with the impetus to keep them in better condition in the future.

Dentist

If, by any chance, you suffer from a breath that is not as fresh as it might be, your teeth may be to blame. In any case, have a check-up if you haven't seen your dentist for six months. If you have ill-shapen teeth, do consider the possibility of having a new and more attractive set.

Corsetière

Either have a chat with the qualified fitter in a local store in the privacy of a cubicle, or visit a corsetière who represents one of the leading corset firms and who works from her home. You will find their names listed in the telephone directory. Whatever your size or age, be you seventeen or seventy, advice from a fitter is invaluable. It can literally make all the difference between a flabby and a firm bosom, a sleek line or a ripple of bulges.

Now, the *things* you should do.

Stand up straight, tail and tummy pulled in, head held firm and straight. Notice the difference this makes to your general appearance. Your midriff feels firmer and hips and tummy look slimmer. Start thinking tall from now on. If you are naturally so, thank your lucky stars, and don't, whatever happens, start slouching around in an effort to look smaller! Your height is nothing to be ashamed of.

Try your newly prescribed make-up in the quiet of your bedroom or bathroom. Experiment with eyebrow shapes too. Look in a fashion magazine and carefully copy a variety life-size on to greaseproof or strong tissue paper. Cut them out and hold them over your own eyebrows until you find a shape which suits you.

Good grooming starts in your wardrobe. It is better to have one or two perfect outfits which have been altered to fit, are correctly hemmed and with neat linings, rather than many bits and bobs which never quite match up into one effective whole.

Spring-clean your wardrobe, shoe shelves and drawers. For once in your life do not be tempted to hoard. Dispose of all the things that you haven't worn in many ages: blouses that are too small, a skirt that doesn't quite fit, old shoes, a hat that is out of fashion. If they are in a reasonable condition they would be gratefully received by a charitable organisation.

Clean, polish and brush your shoes and handbags. If you are not often using certain bags, wrap them in tissue. Wash out any soiled gloves and starch freshness into bedraggled scarves.

Take soiled suits, coats and dresses to the cleaner, and resolve to keep them well-sponged and pressed later. Have down-at-heel shoes repaired.

Tidy up beads, bracelets, dress rings and brooches. Clean real gems if necessary. You can find full details in Chapter 12.

Finally, treat yourself to a few early nights. It is surprising how much better you look and feel with a few extra hours of sleep.

Twenty Ways to be Beautiful 'though almost Broke!

Do not worry unduly if you cannot afford to buy some of the more expensive cosmetics and beauty preparations. You can make many for yourself by using the products of nature. Following is a list of beauty aids which need barely affect your purse, and may only require a trip to the kitchen vegetable basket, the fruit bowl or the pantry.

1. *Eye Lotion.* Add just a few drops of witch-hazel extract (distilled), to an eye bath of barely warm water.

2. *Bath Tonic.* Add fresh herb or oil of thyme to your bath water for a refreshing and soothing dip.

3. *Skin Cleanser* (*a*). Pat on the top of the milk. This is very good for dry skins.

4. *Skin Cleanser* (*b*). Smooth on yoghourt.

5. *Skin Cleanser* (*c*). Dilute honey in milk, using one measure of clear honey to nine of the liquid.

6. *Hair Rinse* (for fair or mousey hair). For your final

11

rinse add the juice of a whole lemon to a pint of warm water.

7. *Face Tonic.* Smooth honey into your face and leave for about a quarter of an hour before rinsing off with warmish water. This is an excellent complexion tonic if you don't mind feeling sticky for a few minutes.

8. *Skin Bleach.* Rub the inside of fresh lemon peel on to your elbows to whiten the skin, or use half a lemon, rubbing the flesh on to your skin.

9. *Skin Freshener.* If you have a normal skin, i.e. one that is not dry, greasy or combination, use apple juice as a moist freshener after cleansing. Dry skin types should use a sliced grape. Use a piece of fresh potato if your skin is greasy.

10. *Lacquer.* You can make a perfectly harmless fixative for your hair by partly filling a plastic spray bottle with lemon juice. Have a little patience while it dries as it takes longer than manufactured lacquers.

11. *Tooth Cleanser.* Pure, unsweetened apple juice will clean your teeth, as it contains acids which have a good cleaning action without being abrasive.

12. *Cooling Lotion.* Smooth fresh sliced cucumber over your face in hot weather. If you have a mechanical juicer the fresh cucumber juice makes an excellent skin tonic and after-bath freshener.

13. *Footbath.* To ease tired feet which have been on the go all day, mix one tablespoonful of dry mustard to a paste with cold water. Allow to stand for a few minutes, then add to a basin of water which is as hot as you can stand it. Keep your feet in it for ten to fifteen minutes.

14. *Face Mask* (*a*). Blend fine oatmeal with the top of the milk and smooth it over a dry-skinned face for ten minutes, longer if skin is greasy. Wipe off with a damp cloth or sponge.

15. *Face Mask* (*b*). If you have a greasy complexion,

dab well beaten egg white over your face and neck and let it dry out. Wash off with warm water.

16. *Skin Softener*. Fill a muslin bag with fine oatmeal and hang it in your bath.

17. *Hair Conditioner* (*a*). Use rainwater to wash your hair if you cannot afford a tube of hair conditioner cream. It will add a sleek glossiness to your hair.

18. *Hair Conditioner* (*b*). Massage a softly beaten egg into your hair after washing, and make sure you remove all traces before setting.

19. *Hand Softener*. Massage warm olive oil into your hands and smooth in around the nails.

20. *Fresh Air*. Never underestimate the value of fresh air. A good walk will give your cheeks a better glow than any form of rouge.

When pennies really count, remember that you will always remain attractive and pleasant to be with if you are well groomed, and keep yourself fresh and tidy, with well-brushed hair.

Save money by sponging and pressing clothes regularly, to cut down on cleaner's bills. Take care to use a cloth between fabric and iron if you are pressing any material on the outside (except for cotton and linen), and do not press hard on inside seams, as they will show through.

It helps to realise that basic beauty comes from deep inside of you. It is not guaranteed with money and unlimited cosmetics. It is all a part of how you feel, act, move and talk.

2

DON'T CAMOUFLAGE, CULTIVATE!

Take another look at yourself in the mirror. It is quite a thought to realise that there is no one, anywhere, quite like you. There is no one in all the world who looks, feels and thinks exactly as you do. Therein lies the vital clue to your success.

Be yourself. No famous or beautiful woman is ever a copy of any other, she is always an individual in her own right. There is only one Bardot, one Taylor, one Loren or Lollobrigida, and only one you.

You must never underestimate yourself if you want to be an original. Complete honesty about your face and figure does not necessarily mean success in looks. It can be the first hurdle. How many times, for instance, do tall girls say to themselves: "I can't wear high heels, I'd better keep to flatties," and how many older women refrain from using lipstick or nail varnish because they mistakenly believe that it is "not done" at their age?

Tall girls should not disregard their potential. Heels were made to show off legs, and tall girls have plenty of leg worth showing. There is a certain glamour about an older woman who knows how to use make-up to her best advantage, confident in the fact that a medium lipstick adds a touch of youthful colour to her face, and pale varnish will help to beautify hands that have become lined with housework.

Think positively: I am tall, and I will make the most of my luck, or, I am older and I will make the most of my experience.

14

In order to look outstanding, you must be prepared to experiment with yourself. If you have never worn make-up before (this could particularly apply to an older woman or to a teenager), explain this to the beauty consultant in your local store and ask her to prescribe the appropriate cosmetic shades. Buy a small selection (there are some firms which specialise in very low budget prices which are ideal), and practise using them at home.

Set aside one evening in which to take stock of yourself. With pencil and paper to hand, credit what you believe to be your good points on one side and debit your faults on the other. If you have a friend whom you can rely upon, it would be a good idea to ask her in case you have missed anything out!

Once you have done this, determine to take even more care of your assets and start at once to cultivate, rectify or minimise your faults.

For example, take a girl who is described as "mousey." Her hair colour is neither one shade or another. By nature her temperament is of the shy retiring kind, although she is not without "fight." Her clothes are usually combinations of "safe," rather than inspiring, colours.

The mousey girl usually hides her light under the proverbial bushel when, in reality, she could be sought after for her serenity, and sudden flashes of wit. She should accentuate her features a little more with darker eyeliners and artificial lashes, clear, well defined lips, and hair that is brightened with a honey-coloured rinse. She should switch from safe to subtle colours that will actually make her pale skin and ordinary hair look exciting, rich olive, deep slate blue, or mustard gold, for example.

It is far more effective for a mousey girl to play up and make the most of her colouring than to start wishing she were blonde, raven or red-haired. Now that colour rinses offer so many colour variations, blondes, ravens and redheads are found everywhere. There can be individuality **in** a lovely mouse.

THE QUALITIES OF BEAUTY

As all the great poets, artists and writers will tell you, the beauty of a woman lies not only in her looks but in the qualities which she possesses. They include:

Vitality
The real meaning of this was captured by Edna Ferber, author of *Showboat* when she said: "To be alive is a fine thing. It is the finest thing in the world, though hazardous. It is a unique thing. It happens only once in a lifetime. To be alive, to consciously know that you are alive, and to relish that knowledge—this is a kind of magic." If you go through life feeling like this, you can rest assured that you have vitality.

Happiness
A happy woman is never ugly, because happiness in itself has a radiance that is beautiful. If you are not happy in your job, take the plunge and change it once and for all. Do something that you really want to do and you will never regret it, even if you are not entirely successful. It is always better to have tried and failed than never to have tried at all. Happiness is also giving, whether it is a smile, or a surprise meal for your mother, or an hour's conversation with an aged neighbour.

Individuality
Don't wear a certain fashion because it is "in" if it doesn't suit you, and never be afraid to disagree with everyone when they praise a television programme or a book, if

you honestly didn't like it. Try to stop worrying what other people think about you. If you want to learn Chinese, go to India on a bicycle or stay at home painting pictures, instead of joining a morning coffee round-up every day, then do so.

Tenderness
This is part and parcel of the warm-hearted woman who is thoughtful about old people, kind to animals and friendly with children. It is typified by the woman who stops in the rush of midday shopping to smile and give a small donation to an old man playing an accordion in the street, and in a teenager who finds time to see a child across the road.

Serenity
From now on, make a resolution never to worry about small, trivial things. When you have prepared a meal for two and your husband comes home with two friends, give every appearance of being unruffled, no matter how you feel under the surface. When you are dressed for the theatre and your boyfriend decides to take you to a flood-lit football match instead, relax, and set out to enjoy yourself. In all probability you will. "Nothing," said Hollywood producer, Samuel Goldwyn, Jnr., "destroys charm faster than a woman showing her nerves. You can say it all in two words: Don't panic!" You have been warned!

Graciousness
A teenager who respects her parent's wishes with a good face, is learning the art of graciousness. An older woman who accepts her maturity with thankfulness, as her right-ful due, already has it. If you wish to acquire it, be your-self at all times. Show consideration for others, and

never surround yourself with artificial airs and graces. Learn also, to respect the opinions of others as well as your own.

SEVEN DEADLY FAULTS

Nothing destroys a woman's natural beauty quicker than laziness, false modesty, jealousy, tactlessness, boredom, an obtrusive manner or vulgarity. These are the Seven Deadly Faults which you should guard against at all costs.

Laziness
This covers a multitude of sins like an unkempt appearance, a slovenly home or slackness at work. It is a well-known fact that the majority of people only work at one third of their capacity. Almost everyone is capable of doing so much more and consequently living life to the full. Look around and you will see that it is the active woman who takes a pride in her appearance, has many interests, enjoys home-making or is an efficient secretary or sales girl, who stays younger, longer.

False Modesty
This ranges from automatic disgust registered at the sight of a nude in a painting to a loud "tut tut" when two people embrace in a stage play. It was Shakespeare who said that there is nothing good or bad in this world, but thinking makes it so. You will find the world a much happier place if you have a broadminded outlook. However, in passing, it should be mentioned that there is such a thing as natural feminine modesty, which is important to a girl. It is this which prevents her from "throwing herself" at the opposite sex, wearing extra low necklines or skirts that reveal every stitch of her stocking tops!

18

Boredom
Mental or physical activities are the only antidotes to this. A bored woman *is* boring. An interested woman is always interesting to other people. If you are in danger of becoming bored with life, make an all-out effort to do something really different. Try a new hobby; there are plenty of ideas on the shelves of your local library. Go to night school and learn how to make jewellery or pottery or even start a typewritten or duplicated news-sheet in your block of flats or street, collecting all the latest news, ideas and observations of the people around you. Action creates enthusiasm, and that is another part of that important quality, vitality.

Obtrusiveness
There is nothing more effective for destroying femininity and beauty in company, especially that of men, than a thrusting personality. So do not try to be the centre of attention at all times. The silent woman who listens to others sympathetically and intelligently, is far more likely to retain attention in the long run, than the one who chatters away incessantly.

Vulgarity
This often occurs when a woman tries to act or talk on a level with the opposite sex, telling doubtful jokes and, in general, completely disregarding the fact that she is a woman. Remember that it is also vulgar to talk loudly in public places, such as cafés or on buses, or to sit with your legs crossed and showing your new blue suspenders. Keep your skirt at knee level, not inches above.

THE SEVEN AGES OF BEAUTY

"One man in his time plays many parts," said Shakespeare, "his acts being seven ages." And so it is with a woman too. Each age offers individual joys and advantages to the woman who is prepared to adapt herself, and accept an increase in years as a blessing rather than a burden.

First of all we have childhood, from birth until twelve or thirteen. This is a time of anticipation, excitement and imagination. It is a castle under the kitchen table, long holidays and seeing the snow and sea and a bee on a flower for the first time. And childhood beauty lies in a mother's hands. She must see to regular dental check-ups, plenty of sleep, food with more fruit than sweets, nourishing brown bread, well-brushed and cut hair and correctly fitting shoes. She should also teach the child the importance of discipline. Never be afraid to say "No" in response to "I want!"

Then we have the impressionable years from thirteen to nineteen. The early teens are a time of mental and physical change in a young girl, who will feel happier if her mother explains to her that menstruation is a milestone in her life, and something of which she need never feel ashamed. Freshness and fragrance are naturally of paramount importance. Be scrupulously clean and spend a few shillings on a refreshing toilet water instead of a new record once in a while!

Acne sufferers should have a doctor's advice, and also take advantage of the many medicated creams which are now available for this complaint. It is a big help to take plenty of vitamin A including dried apricots, cream cheese, rose hips, egg yolks, lettuce, mint, parsley, spinach, lemon rind and juice, orange juice and watercress.

A light, but properly fitting bra is another essential, to

be bought and worn as soon as development has started.

For many girls the late teens bring first jobs, the thrill and sadness of falling in and out of love, of being on top of the world one minute, and way down at the bottom the next. How you think, react and eat, at this time, can easily affect your whole life, for it is now that your roots are well implanted.

A nibble at a carrot will pay more figure dividends than eating sweets between meals. If you must smoke, keep it at a minimum, but it is much healthier to leave the habit alone. Cultivate more interests and make sure that you include a sport in your weekly routine. For make-up keep to light colours and clear lipsticks. Think feminine and be feminine. This is, or at least it can be, one of a woman's prettiest ages, so if you want to wear long pants choose a hothouse pastel colour with a glamorous sweater, rather than drab denims and a black pullover.

Between nineteen and thirty we have the age of flair, a time of new freedom, adult attitudes and independence. Wardrobes should be more organised as the twenties progress and should include well-fitting girdles, a crisp little hat, longer gloves, smart polished shoes and a perfectly tailored black or dark dress or two-piece that will sail right through a day and into the evening.

After the age of twenty-five it is a good plan to start using a moisturiser cream on your face and to work out a short exercise routine for every day, to complement a saner approach to food, which allows for the odd splurge here and there, but makes up for it with dieting and fruit juice the next day.

Thirty to forty is the smooth age, when a woman is in prime condition. Health is more settled and outlook more balanced. You have a confidence and an energy that makes you say: "If only I could be seventeen and know what I know now!"

Concentrate on an immaculate appearance and better accessories. Good handbags, shoes and gloves are worth pounds to you in looks, even if you cannot afford an expensive suit. Invest in a long evening skirt instead of slacks for evening relaxation with the television, and think more in terms of glamour. Use handcream every single time you wash, and nourish your face every night. Keep up with a daily exercise plan to ward off a middle-age spread.

The dramatic age arrives with the forties and fifties. Now you know all the tricks of the trade, and have the skill and the right to wear dramatic clothes and jewellery. As children grow up it is time to look out for new interests, particularly those that may be shared with your husband. The menopause need hold no major worries if you have a check-up with your doctor, learn to really relax, especially for a while after lunch, and possibly take a herbal preparation to soothe nervous conditions and keep your blood in good order. Combat figure flabbiness by constantly pulling in your tummy muscles and walking well. Many towns have inexpensive slimming and muscular tone-up salons where you need not undress completely. They are well worth a visit.

When you reach the fifty to sixty age, time is almost your own once more, so don't waste a minute of it! Keep your mind active and remember that good humour can now be one of your greatest assets.

Beware of drab colours and old-fashioned shoes. You can look handsome in fresh, light coloured suits or rich greens, blues and lilacs, with neutral accessories. Rejuvenating creams are worth every penny in morale and appearance, as is a regular trip to the hairdresser to keep grey hair soft and smoothly styled around the face. Grooming, as always, should be meticulous. A glass of warm water taken first thing every morning will help to prevent the constipation which so often occurs at this age, often due to lack of exercise.

Finally, the serene age. This can be a wonderful period in a woman's life. It can take on a new bloom if a calm outlook is cultivated and you continue to be interested in all and everything. Make-up should be feather light, and lips and eyebrows should be made up with special care to prevent smudginess. If money happens to be short, and you cannot afford many cosmetics, do remember the tips in chapter 1.

In all the age groups, a woman will be a happier person if she realises that youth is not a birthday that falls under the age of twenty, but a state of mind that exists in every age.

3

FIGURING IT OUT

Figure improvement is possible immediately! How are you sitting now? Hunched over a table? Slumped in a chair? How do you stand at a bus stop or in a queue? Hip pushed out to one side, all your weight unevenly distributed? And walking? Do you slouch along? It is surprising how many of us are guilty of one or all of these major figure failings.

Try sitting straight, with your spine firm against the chair back, and walk erect with most of your outs, tummy and behind, pulled in. Take a sidelong glance at yourself in a shop window and see the immediate improvement. This is the real meaning of posture.

If you decide to add a few exercises to your day, you will find your figure improving within six or eight weeks. You will breathe better, feel less tired and far more alive. On cold days your circulation will be in tip-top form and your toes will feel warmer.

Once the first two or three days of a new exercise routine are over, those initial aches and pains, caused by seldom used muscles getting into trim again, will go. A sense of well-being will take over and many of your physical and mental tensions will disappear. If you doubt my words see for yourself!

If you want company for some of your exercises, inquire about your nearest League of Health and Beauty or Y.W.C.A. fitness classes, both of which cater for all ages. I have seen women old enough to be grandmothers, gaining and maintaining trim figures that leave even teen-

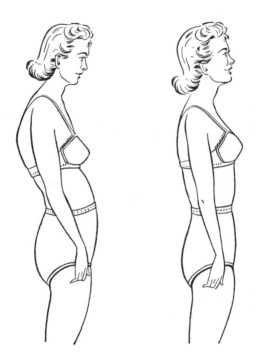

Good posture will correct many figure faults instantly.

agers envious. However, if you are in an older age group, it is a good idea to check with your doctor before joining one of these sessions, especially if you are not used to exercise.

Now is the time to forget the figure of Gina Lollobrigida, Marlene Dietrich and the local beauty queen and

25

concentrate on making the most of *your* figure and size. A small thin girl who wants to look like Sophia Loren is beaten before she starts!

How much better it is to work towards a well-balanced series of measurements for your own figure.

It may help you to know that even the late Marilyn Monroe did not have a perfect figure proportionately speaking, her measurements being 37-23-34. Correct balance means bosom and hips that are approximately equal in size, with a waist ten to twelve inches smaller.

Here is a chart to give you an idea of the right measurements for your height.

Height (in stockinged feet)	Bust	Waist	Hips
4' 10"			
4' 11"	32-34	20-23	33-34
5'			
5' 1"			
5' 2"	34-35	21-23	34-35
5' 3"			
5' 4"			
5' 5"	35-38	22-25	35-37
5' 6"			
5' 7"			
5' 8"	37-40	24-27	37-38
5' 9"			
5' 10"	37-41	25-28	37-40
5' 11"			

The difference between each of the measurements makes allowance for various bone structures. You can tell your own particular size by measuring your wrist. A small frame has one of approximately five-and-a-half inches in circumference; a medium, six inches, and a large is up to six-and-a-half or seven inches.

IDEAL WEIGHTS FOR THE VARIOUS BODY STRUCTURES

Height	Age Group 15 to 24		Age Group 25 to 34		Age Group 35 to 44		Age Group 45 and over	
	st.	lb.	st.	lb.	st.	lb.	st.	lb.
	9	4	9	11	10	5	10	12
5′ 0″	8	1	8	7	9	0	9	6
	6	12	7	3	7	9	8	0
	9	6	9	13	10	7	11	0
5′ 1″	8	3	8	9	9	2	9	8
	7	0	7	5	7	11	8	2
	9	10	10	1	10	11	11	4
5′ 2″	8	6	8	11	9	5	9	11
	7	2	7	7	7	13	8	4
	9	13	10	5	11	0	11	7
5′ 3″	8	9	9	0	9	8	10	0
	7	5	7	9	8	2	8	7
	10	3	10	10	11	5	11	10
5′ 4″	8	12	9	4	9	12	10	3
	7	7	7	12	8	5	8	10
	10	6	10	13	11	9	12	1
5′ 5″	9	1	9	7	10	1	10	7
	7	10	8	1	8	9	8	13
	10	11	11	4	12	0	12	6
5′ 6″	9	5	9	11	10	6	10	12
	7	13	8	4	8	12	9	3
	11	1	11	8	12	4	12	11
5′ 7″	9	9	10	1	10	10	11	2
	8	3	8	8	9	2	9	7

IDEAL WEIGHTS FOR THE VARIOUS BODY STRUCTURES

Height	Age Group 15 to 25 st. lb.	Age Group 26 to 34 st. lb.	Age Group 35 to 44 st. lb.	Age Group 45 and over st. lb.
	11 6	11 13	12 9	13 3
5' 8"	9 13	10 5	11 0	11 7
	8 6	8 11	9 5	9 11
	11 9	12 3	13 0	13 8
5' 9"	10 2	10 9	11 4	11 11
	8 9	9 1	9 8	10 0
	11 13	12 7	13 4	13 12
5' 10"	10 6	10 13	11 8	12 1
	8 12	9 4	9 12	10 4

In many cases exercises and sensible eating will eventually give you a better figure without going on a slimming diet.

Figure Trimmers

The Bosom. Exercise does not add actual inches to your bosom, but it can and will improve the general shape by strengthening the pectoral muscles across your chest. It isn't for nothing that many beauty queens go in for minor forms of weight lifting! If you have a small bosom your measurements will show what appears to be an increase due to better development of those chest muscles, and a larger bosom will benefit by becoming firmer and less flabby.

Try this exercise daily: sit down with your legs crossed and back straight. Now place the fingertips of your left hand on your left shoulder and sweep forward, up and back, making as large a circle as you can. Continue ten times, then repeat with the right hand.

28

Here is another: in a sitting position, grip your right wrist with your left hand and your left wrist with your right hand. Move your arms until they are level with your bosom. Now exert force and push your hands in the direction of your elbows, making sure that you feel a tightening of the pectoral muscles. Do this about fifteen times.

Flabby Arms. Hold your arms straight out on either side of you, with palms uppermost. Clench your hands firmly, moving them forward and almost under at the same time, but still keeping your arm straight. Open your hands, clench and repeat about ten or fifteen times.

Waistline Ways. Stand upright, legs apart and slide right arm down right leg, bringing left arm in a curve over your head. Press down with right arm. Do the same with the other side, about five times at first and increase to ten or twelve.

Still with your feet slightly apart, try this exercise. Hands on your waist, bend over forward, keeping your back level and rotate the upper half of your body, moving forward, to the side, back and up again. Do this ten times increasing to twenty.

Hip and Thigh Lines. Stand upright. Rest your right hand on your waist and your left on a chairback. Point your right leg and toe (keeping it that way throughout the exercise) and swing it forward, down and back about five or six times. Repeat with other leg, putting your right hand on the chairback this time. Build up gradually until you are touching the twenty to twenty-five mark.

For the second exercise keep one hand on a chairback as before, and lift your heels off the ground. Now give your knees a full bend and bounce up and down with an easy rhythmic motion (keeping your feet on the ground).

The third exercise is hard to beat for results. It is best known as "The Bicycle." Lie down flat on the floor, lift your legs straight up and balance your body by resting your hands on your waist, with your upper arms straight on the floor. Now pretend that you are taking part in the Tour de France and cycle away as fast, and as firmly as you can, with long brisk strokes.

While many women want to *lose* inches around the thighs and hips, many others want to *gain*. The following exercise is for them only.

Stand upright, arms akimbo, and move forward with your left leg, bending it and pressing down, keeping the other leg outstretched behind (think of a lunge position in fencing). Move forward with the right leg and repeat the action.

Tummy-smoothers. Lack of exercise is one of the prime causes of protruding tums. A strong girdle will certainly help matters, but this is not the natural solution. It is up to you to pull in your tummy muscles as often as possible during the day, as you go about your work, either standing, walking or sitting. You will also find that this action automatically gives you a better posture.

Here are two exercises. Lie on the floor on your back. Lift up your head and bend your right leg. Take hold of the calf with both hands and draw it firmly towards your face. Repeat with the other leg. Try this about five times at first and gradually increase.

Remain on your back for the second exercise. Keeping your legs straight, raise them together until they are sloping up at an angle from your trunk. Slowly move them down a little, hold the position, then continue slowly down. You will be able to feel the stomach muscles tautening. This is not an easy one at first, but it becomes easier the more you persist.

Leg-toners. Sit on the floor, legs stretched out in front of you, and touch your toes with both hands, keeping legs straight.

30

Take It Easy

Do not overdo any of the exercises in a fit of enthusiasm at the start. Take them gradually and let your tired muscles get used to action once more. If you feel particularly painful, you know you have overdone it, so ease up. Expect, however, a little stiffness at first, which will soon go.

Your best plan is to couple the exercises of your choice with the general fitness group in Chapter 4. Do them *every* day! It's no use expecting results if you do them in fits and starts.

Watch your breathing and try to keep it deep and even with all exercises.

Incidentally, while on this subject of exercise, looking the other way when cream buns are handed around is not the only way to a good figure. A general exercise, such as tennis or swimming, can dispose of a few hundred calories in an hour!

Aids to Trimness

Did you know that:

—you can buy individual home massagers for under three and four pounds? Some are battery driven and need no flex. Accessories are also available which help to smooth away facial wrinkles, stimulate your scalp and tone your skin generally.

—for under fifteen shillings you can buy a roller point massager. Made up of fat dispersing graduated pressure cones, it is effective on nearly every part of the body.

—also for under fifteen shillings there is a stretch cord home exerciser which enables you to really s-t-r-e-t-c-h. It is especially useful for strengthening the pectoral muscles.

Foundation Facts

Never dismiss a qualified fitter when you go to buy and

try on a new bra, girdle or corset. You may easily be dismissing an even better figure for yourself in the process.

Here is the advice of Mrs. Tessa Seiden, of Rigby and Peller, a leading firm of London corsetières: "Without the help of an experienced fitter, the wearer might easily choose the wrong line for her figure and she might even damage her natural figure beyond correction.

"The flesh must not be pushed up by too tight a girdle, and the girdle should be long enough in the back, otherwise it might ride up. The bra should give the right support, again without being too tight, and the straps should not cut in. Also, the bra should have a good division.

"A corset and bra should hold the figure in balance. A too small bust may need a bra with a definite line. If the bust is a good shape it will make the tummy look flatter.

"New man-made fibres do not always provide enough support on their own. Bones are still necessary for the large figure or the figure with a waist sinking in too much at the back, i.e. 'hollow back.' Strapless garments must have bones if they are to work really well."

Mrs. Seiden recommends that when you try on a bra, you lean forward and then fasten the garment—which will then settle itself. The girdle should be up in front, and down at the back.

A correct foundation garment "wardrobe" should include either two day corselettes and one strapless corselette, or two corsets, four day bras, and one or two strapless bras.

In some instances it is certainly worth a little extra money to have a foundation garment made to measure. So many women still consider this an almost unnecessary luxury, yet they will pay a tailor or a dressmaker to make them an outfit, when the real secret of good garment fit lies in the actual foundation.

The magic of glamour, emphasised by black velvet, a film of veiling, a sparkle of jewels and—a woman who knows the meaning of femininity.

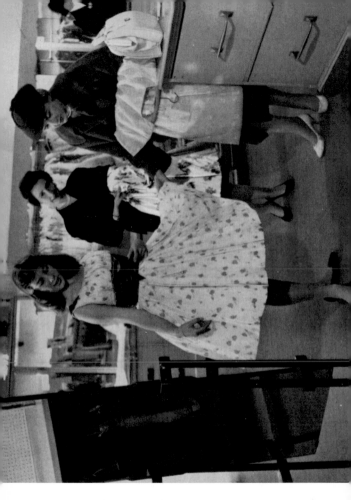

How *not* to dress a plumpish teenager! The full skirt, ruched bodice and cluttered waistline only add inches. A streamlined sheath dress or princess style would trim her figure and give her a well-groomed look.

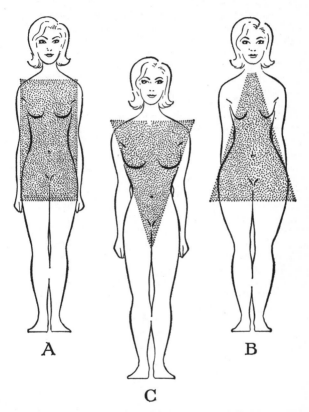

The three basic figure types: A. Average; B. Hip-heavy;
C. Top-heavy.

Basic Figure Types

Before looking for a new foundation garment, it is as well to know your basic figure type. This will probably fall into one of three types.

Average. Here the hips measure about the same as the bust and about ten inches more than the waist. Typical measurements: bust, 36 inches; waist 26 inches; hips 36 inches.

Hip Heavy. Hips may be between 12 to 15 inches larger than the waist, and up to five inches larger than the bust. This figure is built around a big, bony frame, usually long in the leg and body, with wide shoulders and hip-bones, smallish breasts and rather spare flesh except on the hips and buttocks. Sometimes it is known as the Anglo-Saxon or North European figure. Typical measurements: bust 36 inches; waist 27 inches and hips 40-42 inches.

Top Heavy. This type has a slim hipped figure, but a heavy bust. It is usually short and flesh tends to concentrate on the upper half of the trunk. It may be described sometimes as a Latin or Mediterranean type. Typical measurements are: bust 40 inches; waist 28-30 inches; hips 36 inches.

Your basic figure type has nothing to do with size or age. You are born a certain type and will remain that way, variations being provided by accumulation of flesh through bad posture or diet. Remember that each type can be attractive and a trained corsetiere will help you to achieve perfection, by seeing that you buy suitable garments.

4

FOOD, FORM AND FRESHNESS

The four gateways to health and vitality are good food, adequate rest, enough exercise and plenty of fresh air.

Unfortunately, much of today's food is processed almost beyond recognition, and a large amount of the natural goodness and vitamins are "refined" out and artificial vitamins and other additives take their place. With a little thought, however, it is possible to rectify at least some of these points and to let your health benefit accordingly.

Use raw brown Barbados sugar for sweetening instead of white, and if you are a housewife try baking with pure wholewheat flour. It need only take you twenty minutes or so to prepare bread prior to rising and baking, and the majority of recipes are much easier than those for cakes. Wholewheat flour provides an excellent natural roughage for your system, and in addition the bread is a real beautifier, containing natural vitamin B_2, which promotes a clean, clear skin and healthy eyes.

Drink plenty of *natural* fruit juices. And whenever you can, try a meal composed entirely of fruit and vegetables. For example, you could start with an hors d'œuvres of sliced onion and tomato rings (both raw) in a corn or vegetable oil and vinegar dressing, followed by a salad of either sliced orange or pear halves (fresh), topped with grated cheese and parsley and served with chopped cabbage or lettuce leaves. For a dessert, alternate layers of cooking apple and banana, top with brown sugar and bake in a covered casserole for fifteen or twenty minutes. No water is needed.

Instead of drinking cup after cup of tea with sugar and milk, try an equally refreshing herbal tea such as lime flower, which has a delicate flavour and acts as a nerve soother when things get hectic.

Never be tempted to over-eat. It is much better to leave the table feeling just slightly hungry. Always try to relax before a meal if you want the food to do you good, especially if you tend to be on the thin side. A meal taken when you are angry, for instance, will not be fully beneficial.

Only you know how much rest you need. Usually it is an average of eight hours or so. Some need more, others less. Whatever your requirement, try to get an early night at least once a week and relax with a book, or give yourself a leisurely manicure.

If, at any time, you cannot sleep, remember that you are gaining a good amount of rest if you lie there quietly. Should you have a tendency towards insomnia, add three teaspoons of apple cider vinegar to a cupful of honey, store it in a jar and take two teaspoonfuls when you go to bed. This is a natural, safe way of promoting sleep.

Many women, particularly girls who work in big office blocks from nine until five and then hurry into a train or bus and home, forget the bonuses provided by fresh air, especially a better complexion and a more relaxed mind. If you work indoors all day, even to the point of having lunch in the office canteen, do make an attempt to step out for a quick walk. Housewives will feel fresher if they walk to the shops first thing in the morning, prior to their housework. And everyone should try to include a sport of some kind in their weekly routine, which may be anything from archery, golf and boating to swimming, cycling or just plain walking.

Exercising without Effort

Exercises, contrary to general opinion, need not be the formidable early morning disciplines that many imagine! You can exercise if you wish while dusting, shopping, having a bath or sitting at your office desk.

Next time you do the dusting hold in your stomach muscles and then slowly ease them out. Do this as often as you can to keep the muscles firm and your tummy flat. When you bend down to dust the skirting board keep your legs as straight as possible. Don't slouch over the carpet sweeper, but hold your head high and your shoulders back. When you draw curtains or reach to a high shelf, do it gracefully and remember to take full advantage of the stretching movements to keep your midriff firm. Walk on tiptoe barefoot if you want to tone up your calf muscles.

Your bath is an ideal place to do hand and foot exercises. For ankle trimness make circles with your toes. You can do this same exercise under an office desk. It will help to improve the warmth of your feet on cold mornings too! For a variety of hand exercises *see* Chapter 8.

When no one is looking touch the tip of your nose with the tip of your tongue. Whether you can actually do this or not remains to be seen, but the effort helps to prevent a double chin.

Even shopping can be exercise. Carry your bags with outstretched arms and you will improve your arm muscles. People who live in flats with plenty of stairs may feel happier when they realise that stair climbing is wonderful for trimming the legs and their muscles. It never seems so arduous either, if you take it steadily, hold yourself straight and breathe in deeply and regularly.

A Fifteen Minute Fitness Plan

The following is a fifteen minute personal fitness plan which can be adapted to your own requirements and carried out together with exercises for specific parts of your figure (*see* Chapter 3).

Stand in front of an open window or door, arms akimbo. Breath in deeply, hold your breath for 20 seconds and exhale slowly and evenly. Do this a few times before you start your exercises.

Now stand straight, with one hand on a chair back, the other resting on your waist. Slowly raise your outer leg forward. Now lower it and lift backwards, keeping the leg and foot straight and pointed. Swing firmly like this five times, increasing gradually to 20 times for each leg.

Still standing, with your feet apart, now stretch arms out sideways. Turn around to the left, keeping arms and legs straight and swing around until you are facing backwards. Return to forward position and repeat to the right. Do this briskly 20 times from side to side, increasing to about 40.

Sit on the floor with legs outstretched and apart. Lift both arms and turn your body sideways, then bend forward and touch your right toe with your left hand. Up again, turn to the other side and down again, touching left foot with right hand. Make sure that you keep your knees straight and your head well down. Try this four or five times and work up to ten.

The following exercise is not easy to start with, but it is worth the effort as it helps to relieve tension and it also trims the tummy. Lie on the carpet, face downwards. Lock fingers together behind your neck, then raise your head and feet a little until your shape resembles a melon slice, and roll back and forth.

Stand up again, then drop forward, head down and body loose. Swing up and down, taking movement from waist. Rise slowly when you finish. This is another first-class exercise for relaxing you and removing tension.

When doing any exercise breathe evenly throughout.

The best time for your exercises is when you rise. Don't try them before you go to bed or else you may find yourself too invigorated to sleep!

Food and the Figure Conscious

If your weight does not tally with the appropriate figures given in Chapter 3, careful eating may be the answer, and it will pay you to study the following sections.

Certainly you can eat as much as you like of the following: all kinds of meat, steak, roast beef, bacon, salami, etc. Watch sausages and only eat those which are full meat. Fish and shellfish are safe to eat (with the exception of fish fried in rich batter), as are eggs, cheese, some vegetables and fruit (check other sections), dairy foods and poultry.

Occasionally you can eat nuts, bananas, pears and grapes; root vegetables such as carrots, potatoes, beetroot and parsnips, and the podded types such as peas and broad beans. Half a pint of milk a day is in order, and small portions of starch reduced rolls and crispbreads. Other "occasionals" include baked beans, a glass of dry wine, including champagne, sherry, dry vermouth and soda water.

Never eat the following unless you have no alternative: cakes, white bread, biscuits, sweets, chocolates, macaroni, spaghetti, noodles, flour-thickened gravies and sauces, ice cream, tinned and dried fruit, sweet wines, fish in heavy oil, pies, jam, marmalade and honey, dried vegetables, fizzy drinks.

Twelve Aids to Slimming

1. Do not eat prior to going to bed.
2. When you feel like a snack between meals have a small piece of cucumber or cheese (Leicester, Cheddar or Cheshire for instance). No cream cheese.

3. Eat plenty of fresh or tinned tomatoes. Slice them and sprinkle with chopped parsley, or arrange on a bed of watercress as an hors-d'œuvres.

4. Drink a cup of bouillon or vegetable extract prior to a party, so that you will not arrive ravenous and ready to charge through the buffet!

5. Do not eat a meal purely for convention's sake, at lunchtime or at night, if you really don't feel like it. It will do you no harm to have a tomato juice once in a while, and nothing else.

6. Buy some Kelp, a seaweed product, which works two ways: it will help to slim you if that is necessary, and it will help you to put on weight if you are thin.

7. Take a fruit juice for your elevenses instead of coffee. (Fresh if possible.)

8. Try this recipe if you are stumped for a non-fattening hors-d'œuvres for a special occasion. Dice and cook some mixed vegetables such as cucumber, celery and carrot, and leave to cool. Stir two teaspoonfuls of marmite in a pint of hot water. Put a small portion in a cup and dissolve an ounce of gelatine in it, then add the rest of the liquid. Put the diced vegetables into individual moulds and top up with the jelly. Serve on lettuce leaves when set.

9. Use powdered skim milk instead of bottled milk. This contains all the nourishing essentials, with the exception of the animal butter fat.

10. Beware of sandwiches if you have a packed lunch. Take a cold chop with lettuce and tomato; sliced salami, celery sticks, crispbread; a chicken leg with salad, or hard-boiled eggs with cress. With any of these you could have a small tin of tomato juice or a flask of clear soup.

11. Keep to a firm exercise schedule every day.

12. Check with your doctor before you start a slimming diet, and ask for his personal advice and recommendations for you.

Adding the Pounds

Here, too, it is a good idea to see your doctor first of all, in case he can help you in any specific way.

Otherwise you can eat most of the things which are taboo to slimmers. Keep to wholewheat bread where possible because it is far more nourishing and better for your nerves (and nervous people are so often thin). Make sure you have plenty of rest at night, preceded by a snack of biscuits and a sweet milk beverage. Learn to eat slowly. It may also help you to take Kelp which assists in building up tissue.

Incidentally, if you like stout, this could be your answer. I once knew a girl who put on valuable pounds over a twelve month period by drinking a bottle of stout daily, plus plenty of milk!

The Importance of Vitamins

Thin or fat, every woman needs her quota of vitamins if she desires to remain attractive. Whenever possible they should be taken in a natural, rather than an artificial, form.

Vitamin A. This promotes clear skin, good teeth and vision. You often feel tired on waking if you are short of this vitamin. It is found in fish-liver oils, carrots, dried apricots, liver, kidney, rose hips, parsley, water-cress, mustard and cress, lettuce, tomatoes, celery leaves, endives, cheddar and cream cheese, bananas, eggs, oranges, oysters, cabbage, sprouts and ice cream.

Vitamin B_1 gives you vitality, healthy skin and digestion, mental awareness and a ready-to-go-anywhere-do-any-thing feeling. It is found in yeast, wheat bran, mushrooms, peanuts, kidney, liver, grapes, chestnuts, oranges, canta-loupe melon, raisins, raspberries, eggs, milk, watercress, peas, beans, spinach, wheat germ, brown rice.

Vitamin B_2 promotes skin health, vigour and firm bowel

movement. Lack of it can lead to fatigue. It is found in liver, yeast, lean meats, eggs, whole grain, cheese, bacon, green lettuce, peas, watercress, asparagus, carrots, cauliflower, peanuts, nuts, grapefruit, raisins, avocados, prunes.

Vitamin C is good for blood and skin and builds up resistance against colds and other infections. It is found in parsley, blackcurrants, spinach, sprouts, fresh peppers, lemon rind and juice, tomatoes, cabbage, grape juice, bananas, beetroot, molasses, parsnips, cucumber, blueberries, cauliflower, orange juice, watercress, turnips, grapefruits and red currants.

Vitamin D is especially important in young people as it promotes good bones and prevents rickets. It benefits teeth at any age. It is found in molasses, almonds, cheese, watercress, cod-liver oil, herrings, sardines, egg yolk, margarine, dried figs, kale, halibut-liver oil and, of course, sunlight.

Vitamin E. This is an important vitamin concerned with reproduction and is found in wholegrain cereal, eggs, liver, butter, watercress, corn oil.

In order to gain a maximum vitamin intake from your food, cook vegetables in a minimum of water; don't prepare them the day before as many vitamins will be lost; never put soda in a pan of vegetables as it will ruin the vitamins. Frozen vegetables should be placed in pan and cooked before thawing.

A last word: Potatoes are far more nutritious if either baked or boiled with their skins left on them.

Fresh as a Daisy

A cliché maybe, but definitely the nicest way for any woman to be at any time. According to Pliny, soap appears to have been made originally by boiling goat's tallow and causticized wood ashes. The soft potash sap that resulted was converted into hard soap by treating the paste repeatedly with salt.

Today you can buy soaps that not only clean, but scent, deodorise, medicate and nourish your skin. They are, of course, only one part of a fastidious woman's hygiene. Bathing and soaping are not the complete answers to freshness today. Life is faster, and when women and young girls spend much of their time travelling in hot crowded buses or trains, or shopping in busy lunch hours in stuffy stores, extra precautions are advisable.

It is important to remove under-arm hair regularly with either a depilatory cream or a razor, and then after daily washing, to use a deodorant to control odour and an anti-perspirant to check the flow of perspiration. In many cases the two are combined in one preparation. Always read the instructions, as some should not be used immediately after shaving or creaming away under-arm hair.

If you have a tendency to perspire heavily, or you are wearing a dress with tight sleeves, wear dress shields for extra protection.

Always keep the most personal part of your body clean at all times. You can make doubly sure of freshness by carrying a dainty pack of moist, antiseptic deodorant cloths, specially made for this purpose, in your handbag.

Six Bath Plans

The quick in and out bath is fine as a stimulator, but every once in a while, and more often if you can manage it, have a leisurely soak with a book and a cup of tea. Ease your head on to a pillow made out of foam rubber and let the aches, pains and tensions ease away. A bath is one of the finest remedies for the latter or worry and over-work, and far better than tranquilliser pills.

The Stimulator. Try this in the morning, any time during the day, or before going out at night. Use medium hot water, with a pine essence or some cologne poured in under the running tap. Have a brisk sponge down, followed by a thorough towelling. Top off by smoothing body lotion into your skin.

The Invigorator. Pour a teaspoonful of olive or bath oil into a warm bath, and give your body a friction rub with a loofah or bath mitt, until you feel a-tingle all over. This bath works wonders for your circulation, and it wakes you up too, so don't try it before retiring for the night.

The Luxury. Add a frothing bath lotion to warm water (the very look of the bubbles makes you feel good), then settle in for at least 20 minutes, hair up and prettily turbanned, soap, sponge and other necessities to hand on a bath rack. If you decide to read, have a small towel handy to wipe your fingers if they get wet. Towel yourself dry, and splash on a body lotion and clouds of talc.

The Soother. Add one or two pounds of commercial Epsom salts to a hot bath to ease rheumatic pains. The salts help to remove acidity and impurities from the skin.

The Nourisher. Add a teaspoonful of olive oil or a medicated bath liquid to warm water, and swirl around. Sponge yourself gently and soak for a while before drying on a soft towel. This is particularly good for dry skins.

5

BUDGETING FOR BEAUTY

The women of Britain spend many millions of pounds a year on beauty preparations, but many of them are still not looking their best. Why is this? Cosmetic buying so often becomes a habit, and women do not always adapt their choice of cosmetics to their age. An older woman, for instance, may still be using a face cream which she used as a young woman, when in reality she needs something far more nourishing.

On the following pages are four basic beauty budgets for different age groups. They are not meant to be copied slavishly, but should be adapted to individual requirements. If you are uncertain of the cosmetics you need, the lists will provide a guide. Total prices have been gauged according to age. For instance, the older you are, the more you should spend on foundations, perfumes and nourishing creams. A teenager will get by adequately if she patronises the budget price ranges, which go as low as one shilling and sixpence for creams, powders and lipsticks.

Wherever I have mentioned skin freshener, insert astringent if your skin is oily.

Where possible match your talc, toilet water, soap and perfume so that you have a soft all-over fragrance which becomes as much a part of you as a smile or your signature. One item will also help to accentuate another too, so you get more value out of your fragrances.

If you want to keep all your cosmetics together, make a glamorous box by lining a deep wicker picnic basket (they cost under a pound), with pastel coloured or flowered

45

plastic. Stitch in pockets to hold things like brushes and nail files. Prettify the exterior with a gold paint and some velvet or nylon ribbon bows.

Among their beauty aids, women of all ages should have a natural bristle hairbrush and a good comb; two clothes brushes, one for the bedroom and a small one for the handbag; a hair spray, a pretty bath cap and a boudoir cap if necessary to cover night-time curlers; a good stock of cotton-wool puffs for removing make-up and cleansing, and a small razor or a depilatory cream.

The Teenage Budget

For approximately £2 6s. 6d. a teenager can buy tissues, hand cream, emery boards, foundation cream, lipstick, eyebrow pencil, nail polish, polish remover, toilet water, deodorant stick, medicated soap, talc, mouthwash, cosmetic bag for handbag, compressed powder and freshener pads (also for handbag). The most expensive item in the list is toilet water. The majority of teenagers cannot afford an expensive perfume, and a good toilet water at around twelve shillings will fill the bill adequately.

If at all possible, invest in a jar of washing grains for pores and blackheads; eye make-up for evenings; a transparent mask to hold over your face when spraying on hair lacquer; a hair dryer (birthday present perhaps?) and a hair trim once a month.

The Career Girl's Budget

This is aimed particularly at the 20-30 age group, and for a total of about £5 10s. 0d. including a perfume in a measured spray holder, and a small bottle of matching perfume for the handbag, it represents a reasonable investment.

The price covers tissues, hand cream, nail polish and remover, moisturising cream, tinted foundation, loose powder, lipstick, eye make-up (shadow, pencil and mascara); skin freshener, perfume in a measured spray holder to save wastage; cleanser, soap, talc, roll-on deodorant, mouthwash and a cosmetic bag, compressed powder compact, perfume phial, tube of handcream, eye drops, gum massagers, and freshener pads in a box, for handbag use.

It is worthwhile saving to buy a magnifying mirror for perfect make-up; artificial nails and lashes for special occasions; bath oil and friction mitt; an all-in-one make-up in a tube; a nose-shine preventative and regular hair and manicurist appointments.

Always keep a cosmetic bag or plastic tray in your desk drawer, holding extra foundation, etc., in case you are going out after work. Also have a small hand towel, soap, nail brush, needle and cotton and a small packet of aspros handy. Use the gum massagers mentioned in the budget list to strengthen gums and freshen your mouth after meals, and especially after lunch when you may not be able to wash your teeth.

If your job is sedentary, do get up a few minutes earlier in the mornings and do some exercises. Make regular trips to the cleaners to keep your clothes in good condition and always arrive at work looking immaculate. Long trailing hair, excessive make-up and over-long nails are definitely out.

The Housewife's Budget

Don't be tempted to leave your make-up routine if you are going to be indoors all day. A touch of one of the all-in-one make-ups that come in a tube and a dab of fresh toilet water need not take more than a few moments to apply before breakfast, and it will work wonders for your morale. Your husband will appreciate it too.

The budget list which follows will cost you between five and seven pounds according to the price you pay for perfume, toilet water and all-in-one tube make-up, which can cost between six and twenty-one shillings. You will be well-advised to pay around twelve shillings for an effective emollient which pays dividends in keeping your skin soft and line-free.

Looked at from the long term the seven pound budget works out at considerably less per week than 20 cigarettes!

You need tissues, toilet water, skin perfume, lipsticks, loose powder, tinted foundation cream, eye make-up, emery boards, nail polish and remover, rouge, emollient for use under foundation; a tube of all-in-one make-up, hand-cream, skin cleanser, talc, bath essence (something like pine to ease away housework aches); soap, mouthwash, skin freshener and deodorant, plus a cosmetic bag, compressed powder, perfume phial and a box of fresheners for your handbag.

Extras well worth having could include after bath body lotions; a diamond and sapphire chippings nail file which is extra gentle; a facial, hair and manicure appointment every so often; home exerciser aids; nose shine preventative and artificial finger nails for emergencies.

Always freshen up in the evenings with a clean make-up, and make a point of keeping a compact and lipstick, plus some emery boards, in the kitchen, for quick touch-ups before answering the door. Wear household gloves or a barrier cream whenever possible. If you do not wear gloves to peel potatoes, which are notorious for soiling hands, peel the vegetable away from the hand with the knife, so that your fingers are moving over the clean potato underneath the skin. Use hand cream as much as possible.

The Older Woman

The cosmetic requirements for the older woman of 50

No matter whether it is real or fake, keep your choice of jewellery simple. Two well chosen pieces, such as earrings and necklace or necklace and bracelet, look far more attractive than a mass of glitter.

A break for beauty, and an efficient, beauty conscious secretary makes full use of a tidy tray holding her cosmetics which she keeps in her desk drawer.

onwards, are much the same as those for the housewife, with the addition of an anti-wrinkle cream or a contour lifting lotion. These may cost around thirty shillings and, although it may seem a lot at first, it should be remembered that these creams usually last for a long time. Results are often obvious within a short time.

If and when you can afford them, treat yourself to a home rejuvenating treatment. This comes from a French cosmetic organisation and you will be able to obtain details from a leading local chemist. Extra special perfumes are your prerogative now, and it will pay you to have a regular hair and manicure appointment, and a facial every so often if you can manage it. Otherwise give yourself a face mask once a week.

Electric vibratory massagers are useful for home treatment and they help to firm muscles which may not have had enough exercise.

If you are very active learn to put up your feet for a while every afternoon, and enjoy a spell of relaxation.

Tricks of the Trade
Did you know that:

SPOTS, those sudden unexpected blemishes which appear overnight, can be camouflaged if you use a special skin-coloured "lipstick"?

NAIL varnish may be dried with an aerosol spray which also leaves cuticles soft and manageable and keeps unvarnished nails in first-class condition.

FACIAL hair can be removed delicately and perfectly for as little as 10s. 6d. a session, at one of the many clinics specialising in this work throughout the country. It is possible to have a preliminary consultation free of charge.

GRIME which has accumulated on your face as the result of traffic fumes, etc., may be removed without spoiling your make-up by pressing a small linen square on your face.

This is an American idea, and the special squares come in small booklets which are handy for your purse, and they absorb grease and grime instantly. This is also worth remembering for a train journey.

NEGLECTED skins, suffering as a result of age, strain, illness, pregnancy, etc., can be rejuvenated in your own home with the use of shock treatment creams prepared by a French cosmetic firm. Treatment lasts a minimum of four weeks, and there is also one for broken veins, acne and freckles.

MASKS come in all varieties to provide instant tone-ups for tired or winter-drab skin. An oatmeal pack, which will suit almost any skin, is available for under two shillings and it contains enough for two sessions. It leaves your skin almost transparently clear and make-up looks far more effective. There are herbal preparations for sensitive and lined skins; moisture masks for dry skins and others which work in three minutes, making them ideal for use prior to an evening out.

Gilt Edged Securities

Whether you are budgeting for beauty or not, you should try to add a few small luxury-looking items to your handbag, which are pretty and essentially feminine.

If your handbag accidentally falls and spills out its contents, how much better for a passer-by to help you rescue a small gold-backed notebook and pencil; a hand-rolled fine linen handkerchief or a gold key-ring with a tiny seal-skin purse attached. All these are available for under ten shillings.

For under a pound you could buy a small carved cream bone cigarette holder from China; a small gilt and be-jewelled pill box; a neat little portable ashtray with a lid; a slim diary in scarlet, white or black; a packet of attractively printed visiting cards or a slim pigskin wallet.

For under five pounds you could add an elegant square flacon in black and gold holding a famous perfume, and buy a matching case holding a lipstick. If you smoke you could invest in a really slim cigarette case and lighter.

If you look around you will be able to find many such extras for your dressing table or handbag, and the price need only be in the shillings range.

Footnote to Budgeting Beauties
Whatever your age group, it is a good idea to put so much away each week towards compact refills, new lipsticks and creams. Nine times out of ten everything finishes at once, and a shilling or two saved every week will constitute a tidy sum towards replacements.

6

INNER BEAUTY

Money or all the cosmetics in the world will not always make a beauty, because beauty is not always a perfect face. It is something more which attracts people; something that comes from within a person.

If you have ever read Margaret Mitchell's *Gone With the Wind* you may remember the first line of Chapter One: "Scarlett O'Hara was not beautiful, but men seldom realised it."

The clue is in the last four words, "men seldom realised it." Why? Because Scarlett O'Hara's personality was beauty in itself. It was vital, alive and sensitive.

Beauty is the whole of you, body and soul, not a mask of powder and mascara. No matter how perfect a face may be, it will soon lose its enchantment if the owner is continuously jealous, selfish or discontented. It is far better to have a few laughter lines fanning out from the corners of your eyes, than a pucker of lines in the centre of your forehead caused through inner bitterness. Nina, of the popular partnership, Nina and Frederick, the Danish singers, is a perfect example. She has no shortage of laughter lines around her eyes, but rather than spoil her features, they typify the happy woman that she is and certainly add to her attraction.

Even ordinary, day-to-day problems and worries, both large and small, can help to make you a more attractive woman if you tackle them in the right way and take a positive stand for yourself in your approach to them. It is far more effective to promote some action, rather than just to sit around and mope, thinking that things will never be right. This way lies maturity, a wonderful asset for any woman.

Learn to laugh more. Don't sit there straight-faced when someone tells a funny story, even if you have heard it before. Join in the fun and relax. Laughter is infectious. It is meant to be, so don't immunise yourself against it with cynicism or pseudo-superiority. Laughter is to the mind like yeast is to bread. It makes it rise up and feel altogether lighter. A laughing child, a laughing woman, these people have a radiance all their own.

Be interested in the things people have to say and in the things that you do. Tell yourself that life is worth living and you'll soon find out that it really is, no matter what the cynics of the world may say. Have enthusiasm, whether it is for a pattern of frost on a cabbage leaf or a new hobby.

Put your heart and soul into your job or your work at home, and be interested in other people's jobs, especially when they are telling you about them. You can learn something from everyone.

Be understanding. Don't be too quick to run people down or make snap judgments and condemnations without first knowing all the facts. Even if they are not good, still try to be understanding. Do not be short-tempered with old people and try to remember that the young are not so bad as you may think.

When a girlfriend loses her boyfriend to another girl an understanding attitude will help, but an open couldn't-care-less approach would only add further salt to the wound. When a person of any age is distressed or very worried, offer to help, and listen while they unburden themselves, making sure that you always respect the information they may give you in confidence.

Cultivate kindness. It goes a long way. It costs nothing to help a child or an old person across a busy road. It takes only a few minutes longer to do some shopping for a housebound person. It is no skin off your nose to give a cigarette to the old news-vendor on the corner of the street. Make a cup of tea for your mother when she least expects it. Surprise your boyfriend with a packet of cigarettes instead of always expecting everything yourself. Pop a bar of chocolate or a small cigar in your husband's coat pocket for him to discover when he goes out in the morning. Little things, but we all know how much they mean.

In all your dealings, strive to be selfless. Give of yourself without thinking what you will get in return.

A Daily Guide to Inner Beauty

1. Be positive rather than negative in your approach to life and its problems.

2. Don't keep saying "I wish" or "If only." A few dreams are fine, but come down to healthy reality more often and *do* something to make them come true.

3. Think beautiful and you will be beautiful, even if you are a plain Jane. Ban jealousy, envy and kindred thoughts, as they only lead to unhappiness. Does it *really* matter that the girl next-door has a bigger engagement ring, or that the neighbour has a washing machine and you haven't? Remember, you have almost certainly got something which in all probability these people would love to have.

4. Make *time* for living. Time can be five minutes on a city park bench on a warm spring day; a cup of tea after a hard day's work; a quarter of an hour's walk or opening a window to hear a bird sing.

5. Every day stop yourself in your tracks and look at something you know well or take for granted, as though you have never seen it before. Peer at a bud on a tree, marvel for a moment at the water that comes through the tap in your kitchen.

6. Every day, learn to smile a little more and mean it. Smile at a stranger in the street, a mother with two fractious children and a load of shopping, a bus conductor or a sales assistant. If you have ever felt depressed and a stranger has smiled warmly at you for no reason at all you will appreciate its uplifting power.

And who knows where a smile will stop? Once a smile starts it not only beautifies the owner's face, but starts off a chain reaction with nearly everyone who sees it. Smile at one person, and that person will smile at someone else. Try it and see, and don't forget to make it genuine. A real smile comes from the eyes and not just the mouth.

7

FACE TO FACE

The Eyes Have It

Used constantly during our waking hours, eyes are the most expressive parts of a face. They "speak" volumes. They flirt, laugh, cry, show fear, joy, happiness, anger and cunning, all without saying a word. We expect our eyes to go through a day at a typewriter, then on to a show or a night at the television, and always, we expect them to give top performance.

Like everything else, however, they need attention and care. An occasional check-up with an optician does no harm, even if you do not wear spectacles.

Eye Fresheners and Exercises

Tension at the back of the neck (typists are often prone to this complaint) will cause eye strain. To relieve it move your head around in a circular motion about five times each way. It also helps to ease the muscles if you circle your shoulders around a few times.

Next, keep your head perfectly straight and steady and describe a few large circles with your eyes, then roll them up and down and from side to side.

To freshen eyes which are tired as the result of smoky rooms, concentrated reading or writing, squeeze a few drops of eye lotion in each to clear them. If you are at home, clear them in an eyebath of sea water made from sea salt (obtainable from a health food store or a chemist).

During a long cinema show rest your eyes for a moment

A. A chunky framed pair of spectacles to offset an oblong face.
B. Shallow lensed frames, slightly winged, to flatter a round face.
C. Deep lensed frames, with a slight wing effect, for a square face.
D. Delicate oblong frames for a dainty, heart-shaped or triangular
   face.

57

by looking at a dark corner of the cinema or down at your feet, and blink quickly a few times.

Can you see the lines clearly on your television screen? If your answer is yes, then you are sitting too near, so move farther back. Never watch television in a room which is dark, apart from the screen, as this needlessly "draws" your eyes. Always have a lamp on, or leave the curtains drawn in the summer months, making sure that the light does not reflect on the screen. Give your eyes a break during a long night's viewing by cupping them in the complete darkness of your hands for a minute.

In the summer or in anticipation of winter sports holidays, never be tempted to buy cheap sun-glasses. You may save money for a while, but you stand the chance of ruining your vision permanently with poor glasses. If you need them buy a lightly tinted pair from an optician or qualified chemist, and if you normally wear spectacles you should have sun-glasses made to your prescription. Well-made sun-glasses are not a luxury, but an essential.

Should you suffer from headaches or eyestrain after watching television or doing some form of close work, consult your optician. Spectacles can be an asset to a woman's face today, often improving plain features and flattering the perfect.

Use a good, almost dramatic make-up, if you wear spectacles and choose frames to suit the shape of your face. Shallow-lensed frames will counteract a round moon-shaped face, especially if they sweep up a little at the sides. Full, deep-lensed frames, rounded or slightly winged, flatter a square face, and oval shapes need a chunky frame. Delicate oblong or square frames are suitable for triangular and heart-shaped faces, with or without a lower frame to the lens.

If you are still unconvinced that spectacles can enhance your looks, or you are afraid to wear them for active

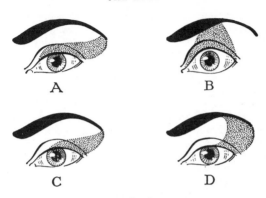

A. Eye shadow for the average eye.
B. Eye shadow for protruding eyes.
C. Eye shadow for close-set eyes.
D. Eye shadow for deep-set eyes.

sports, consider the corneal contact lenses which are only a fraction larger than a sequin and undetectable in use. These are an advance on the original contact lenses which covered the whole eye.

Eye Make-up

Understate rather than overstate eye make-up, unless you want to look like an owl or a clown! If in doubt about a colour choice, key it to the shade of your eyes and see that it tones with your clothes.

Eye Shadow. Apply this after general foundation and prior to powdering. For *close-set* eyes, blend the shadow out and up from the centre of your upper lid. *Deep-set* eyes look best with a soft curve reaching from the outer edge of your lid up to the base of the brow. A touch of white shadow under the chosen shade often helps to counteract a deep-set eye. Give *protruding* eyes more depth by applying colour on the centre of the upper lid, and fade it into a triangle that touches the base of the brow. *Normal* eyes look pretty with a sweep of colour close to the upper lashes and stretching the entire length of the lid.

Shaping the Eyebrow. You will find this much easier if you press a damp warm sponge or clean flannel against your eyebrows first of all, then smooth in a little cream, removing excess with a tissue. Pluck away straggly hairs with tweezers that have been sterilised in hot water, taking them out in the direction that they are growing. To shape in finally, use a special eye pencil with a slightly blunted end (to prevent sharp lines) and fill in with soft feathery strokes. Choose a colour a shade darker than your own hair.

Lashes. If you have sparse lashes don't be afraid to try a pair of artificial ones. They are supplied with effective fixatives. A regular massaging with castor oil will nourish your own lashes. Buy only a small amount of the oil at a time and keep it in a dark bottle to prevent it from turning rancid. Apply mascara to your upper lashes only, concentrating on the outer fringe. Application is easier if you hold your head up and keep your eyes down. Sparse lashes may be thickened by the application of a fluff of powder between the first and second coats of mascara. If you find an excess of make-up on your lashes it is easily removed by gently flicking them on a doubled piece of tissue. Light lashes may be darkened with a special dye which lasts about three months.

Eye Outlines. The outline is drawn in either around the entire eye or on the upper half. You can choose from an eye-liner pencil, or if you find this too hard, use a brush and liquid liner. Buy a shade which accentuates your own eye colour (beware of black if you have deep-set eyes), and draw it finely against your upper lashes. A thicker, darker line will give the appearance of thicker lashes. To make large eyes bigger but small ones smaller draw the line out a fraction at the outer corner. Used carefully, an eye-liner is perhaps one of the best glamour touches after lipstick.

Lip Lines

No woman should be without a lipstick. A clear colour adds the final glow to a face whether the owner is young or old. In order to do full justice to your lips and looks try to build up a lipstick "wardrobe", so that you will have colours to tone with all your clothes. It should include a clear red (to wear with blacks, whites and neutrals); a coral (for greens, browns, oranges and yellows); pink (lilac, blues and pastels); and a deeper red for night wear which will not look pale under artificial light. The latter is also useful if you have a photograph taken. If your lips are on the dry side, an application of lip gloss will add an attractive sheen. Should you be allergic to ordinary lipsticks buy a medicated one which will not affect your skin.

Today's lipstick lines favour a softer, neater look, with a gentle blossoming colour which flatters both skin and eyes. Steer away from lipsticks which are too deep or pale. One tends to age a face and the other looks anaemic.

Before applying your colour, touch your lips with a moisturiser lotion, then lightly powder to make a firm foundation. Use a brush or a slender lipstick to make a clear outline, and fill in the centre carefully. Blot gently with a tissue, add another slight touch of powder and add a second coat of lipstick. Wait a few moments, then blot once more to remove excess.

Thin lips look fuller if you use a lipbrush with a medium to light lipstick (never a dark one which only accentuates a tight line), and carry it very slightly over the natural edge of the lipline. Do not fill it into the corners of the mouth. Add extra fullness to the lower lip by leaving out the basic outline in the centre, thus providing a softer appearance. A *full lower lip* calls for a lipstick outline just inside the natural edge. Use a paler shade of lipstick than on the upper lip. A *small mouth* may be given a better appearance by taking a softly coloured lipstick neatly into the extreme corners, taking great care not to smudge.

Your Teeth

Where beauty is concerned one of your best friends is the dentist. Make an appointment to see him at least every six months whether you think you have anything wrong or not. If you smoke it is advisable to see him every three or four months to enable him to remove nicotine stains.

Healthy gums equal healthy teeth, so keep them in good condition with gentle massage with your finger or a medium toothbrush. It is also a good idea to use medicated gum massagers after every meal, especially if you are away from home. Similar to toothpicks, these are specifically designed for strengthening the gums between the teeth. They are particularly useful in cases of poor or bleeding gums.

Ask your dentist which is the best strength of toothbrush for your teeth and keep it fresh with regular dips in lightly disinfected water. When using it brush the top teeth first with a *down*ward motion, and then the bottom layer, using an *up*ward motion. *Never* go up and down. This is the first step towards gum trouble as you are pushing them away from the teeth all the time and giving acids and mouth bacteria a chance to find a new home at your expense.

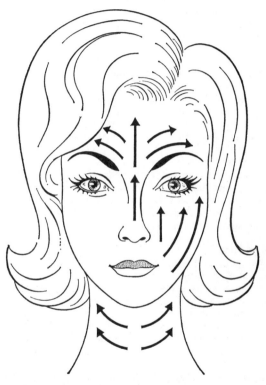

The correct way to apply cream when making up or massaging
your face.

Never delay a visit to the dentist. Equipment is greatly improved and advanced today, and many dentists have high speed drills which take almost all the discomfort out of filling operations. Artificial teeth are made so well that it is virtually impossible to tell them from the real thing, so don't despair if you have to wear them.

If you cannot brush your teeth after every meal, do one of the following: rinse and swill your mouth with water; eat a piece of carrot, raw apple or celery or rinse your mouth with pure unsweetened apple juice.

You can make an efficient mouthwash by adding a teaspoon of salt to a glass of warm water. This is very soothing if you have had an extraction, or if your gums are bleeding or tender.

Finally, make a point of really *using* your teeth. Soft bread, white sugar and soft foods make life too easy for your gums and teeth, so make a point of chewing something crisp and crunchy every day, e.g. apples, carrots or wholemeal bread and biscuits.

Your Face

Good make-up begins with a thorough cleansing, followed by a brisk tone-up in the form of an astringent (for oily skins) or a skin freshener (for normal and dry skins). Next, apply a moisturising cream or lotion suited to your skin type, and tissue off excess. If you have dark skin under the eyes, and you have checked with your doctor to see that nothing is wrong, dab a camouflage cream into the inside corners under your eyes and gently blend it out with your little finger.

Rouge, if carefully blended into your foundation, will look quite natural and is permissible these days. You can choose from a powder cake with a brush, a cream or a liquid, the majority of which are smoothed into your foundation. One or two of the powders are used *after*

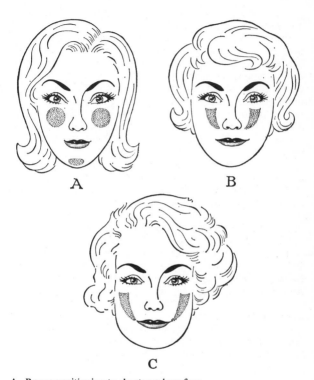

A. Rouge positioning to shorten a long face.
B. A blend of rouge down the inner curve of the cheek for the round face.
C. Rouge applied in a pyramid shape, tapering to either side of the mouth, and suitable for a square face.

powdering. The effect of rouge is to "brighten" the eyes, and to add a pretty bloom to a face.

Rouge also works wonders in rectifying facial faults or problems. Blended down the inner curve of the cheek, it will lend length to a *round* or *plump* face. A *long* face may be shortened with a minute touch on the chin and more on the centre of the cheeks. An illusion of slimness can be obtained on a *squarish* face by applying rouge in a pyramid shape which tapers to either side of the mouth. *Hollow cheekbones* can be counteracted by smoothing or dusting rouge below the cheeks, with only a light touch on the tops.

Over your basic foundation use a tinted one a shade darker than the skin on the inside of your wrist. Take care to keep it off your hairline, and use your astringent or freshener to remove it if it does touch your hair.

Always use loose powder for the first make-up in the day, or before an evening appointment, keeping the cake powder for touch-ups later. Buy a shade which tones with your tinted foundation, fluff plenty on and press firmly in with clean cotton wool. Finally, take a pad moistened with water or freshener and pat it on cheeks and forehead for an extra highlight.

Five Faults Overcome

Shiny Nose or Chin. Apply a drop of anti-shine liquid before powdering. A number of cosmetic firms make this preparation, and although it may seem on the expensive side for a small bottle, it does last a long time.

Long Nose. This can be shortened in appearance by the application of a darker tone of foundation than is used on the rest of your face underneath the tip of your nose.

Large Nose. This will look smaller if you blend a darker tone of foundation or make-up stick down either side.

Scars. Broken veins and similar marks on your face can be safely disguised with a special camouflage cream applied before your tinted foundation and powder.

Reddish Complexion. Use a pale beige foundation under your powder, or slightly pink if your skin is sallow. Touch the top layer of powder with a fluff of green powder (it looks normal on the skin!) as this helps to minimise traces of redness.

Hair

Hair has inspired poets, artists and writers throughout the centuries. It is, and always will be a woman's crowning glory. If her hair is right she feels wonderful and full of confidence. Let it go lank, lifeless and unattended and morale drops dangerously near zero.

Style and expert cutting are more important than all the colours, tints and perms put together. It is the equivalent to hair of a good design to a dress. Health is even more vital than styling, so check your diet if your hair is not as glossy as it should be.

French of London recommends plenty of protein and calcium foods, such as milk and cheese. "Don't," he says, "skimp your meals if you want your hair to look its best. If you are worried about putting on weight, have a glass of milk when you feel in need of a snack, rather than biscuits and buns. Milk contains a lot of the essentials for a well-balanced diet and, taken as a food, is not fattening."

All About Colour

Don't rush into a colour change until you have weighed up the future. A major colour change needs regular touching-up and this takes both time and money.

If you have never changed your colour before, experiment first with a temporary rinse in a darker tone than your present colouring and see if you like it. If not it will disappear with your next shampoo.

Many women are naturally confused when they see so many varieties of colour on the market. The following glossary may help.

Colour Rinse. These are gentle in action, and provide a temporary "lift" to the hair colour and add extra highlights, especially to blondes and fair heads. The colour washes out at the next shampoo. Coloured setting lotions also come under this category.

Permanent Colouring. These will not wash out. There are two types of permanent: the tint, which adds colour and will effectively disguise grey hair, and the lightener, which removes the pigment from your hair. You would be advised to have these done professionally, as a skin test is essential to make sure that your skin is not allergic to the preparations.

Semi-permanents. These are ideal for home use, and they last from about four to seven weeks. Always follow the manufacturer's instructions word for word.

Bleaching. This should be done by a professional hairdresser. This process can completely devitalise your hair if not done carefully. If, however, you merely want to lighten already fair hair just a shade more you could use one of the gentler and more gradual home-lighteners. When you touch up, take care to do only the roots and the darker new hair, or you will make the rest of your hair dry, and the ends will start to split.

Colour and Perms. If you decide to have a permanent wave after lightening your hair, or colouring it in any way, do not omit to tell your hairdresser, as some perms may not react well to bleached or coloured hair.

Be Grey and Like It

Grey hair is no longer a sign of age. Many younger women

find that they can wear prettier colours if they have their hair tinted silver or grey. Far from ageing, grey hair can look more flattering than any other colour so long as it is well cared for and expertly cut.

If your hair is naturally grey and it shows a tendency to yellowness, there is every call for a grey or pastel blue rinse. There is also a special perm for grey hair which includes an anti-yellow pill.

Simplicity of cut and style, with short soft waves turning into the face and a gentle movement across the forehead, are the secrets of success with grey, and they prevent a "hard" appearance. Remember, too, to use a charcoal, grey or silver eyebrow pencil for your eye make-up.

Putting Life into Your Hair

If you suffer from dry, flighty hair that will not stay put, start a brushing campaign to stimulate the scalp and its oils. Use a natural bristle brush and exercise your scalp by resting on your bed on your tummy with your head hanging over the edge, then brush firmly starting at the nape of the neck. The blood will go to your head and enliven the whole scalp.

If your hair lacks bounce, one of the quickest ways of revitalising it is to have a good cut by a professional hairdresser every five or six weeks.

An excess of sun makes hair dry, so prevent this by wearing a sun hat or scarf when sunbathing, and after sea-bathing rinse or wash your hair in tap water to remove the salt, and add a conditioning cream or rinse to keep it glossy. Excessive use of hair sprays can also damage the minute scales of the cuticle or "overcoat" of the hair strand, so make sure that it is brushed out daily. There are a number of shampoos on the market that will loosen lacquer.

Greasy hair can be improved if the scalp is massaged with a little cologne, and the hair may be quickly revived with a puff of dry shampoo, which should be left for a few minutes and then brushed out.

Maintaining a Trouble-free Set

A trouble-free hair-do is a combination of a good shampoo and set followed by careful attention until the next one.

If you shampoo your hair at home buy a shampoo suitable for your hair condition, i.e. greasy, normal, dry or dandruffy, use a conditioner every so often, and always dry with a hair dryer, never in front of a fire or an electric stove as this will dry out the natural oils. It is better to let your hair dry naturally in the air rather than do this.

After washing, set your hair in rollers, using small ones where you need extra body, usually at the front and sides, and larger ones elsewhere. Use clips for short pieces. Pull the hair on the top of your head carefully, but firmly, in the opposite direction before rolling back into place, making sure that the roller is comfortably placed on the head and covering the roots. Stretch side sections of hair straight up first and then roll downwards. This keeps the strands even and straight and provides extra bounce when it is unpinned.

When your hair is absolutely dry, brush it all back, regardless of the style, before easing it into the required shape. A touch of conditioner will help to stay flighty hair.

To keep your set in trim condition use a brush regularly. Odd comb flicks here and there never give a professional appearance. Brush it up from the sides and back until it tapers almost to a point. This action "locks" the hair shafts and in itself provides extra body. Finally, ease down and into place with a tail comb.

Hair Problems

If you have excessive dandruff see your doctor or a tri-chologist, in case it is caused by a diet deficiency or a health problem. If you are sure that it is due to none of these reasons you can treat it yourself with a medicated shampoo. A short style will also help.

Naturally thin hair, described as baby fine, benefits from frequent club cutting. Careful back combing (take a few strands at a time and brush or comb it lightly down-wards from the tip) adds body and gives the impression of more hair than there actually is. Perming will also make it easier to handle.

Should your hair fall out more than it should, consult a trichologist for advice and treatment.

8

THE BIG FOUR

Your Hands

It is open to conjecture whether or not palmists really can tell the future from your hands, but it is possible in many instances to tell the kind of work you do by looking at them. A housewife and a nurse so often have reddened or rough hands through constant contact with water. Typists may have poor nails. The model girl usually has immaculate hands because she rarely uses them in her particular job, other than for expression and gesture.

However, no matter what your work, it *is* possible to improve your hands if you are willing to spend a little time on them. A once-a-week manicure is a must, and here, for your guidance, is a step-by-step plan for a professional one in your own home.

You will need: long emery boards, cotton-wool tipped orange sticks, a nail brush, hand cream, oily cuticle remover, oily polish remover, manicure scissors, a dish of warm soapy water, cotton-wool and a soft towel, plus, if you need either, a base coat or nail strengthener, a top coat and a white nail pencil for use if you choose a clear varnish or none at all.

Soak a pad of cotton-wool with oily polish remover and take off old polish by stroking it over the nail from base to tip. File your nails with the coarse side of an emery board, moving from the corner to the centre tip and round off with a gentle oval, never a point. Don't use a sawing motion or file down too far at the sides as you will weaken the nail. Finish off with the smooth side of the emery board.

Wash your hands and nails in the soapy water, using a brush to clean the nails. Soak your fingers for about three minutes then dry well, at the same time gently pushing back the softened cuticle with a corner of the towel.

Dip a cotton-wool tipped orange stick into cuticle remover and work carefully around each nail base, then wash again and dry thoroughly. Trim off any minute excess skin at nail corners with the scissors. Never cut the cuticles, as this will make them grow thick and unsightly.

Now is the time to use a base coat if you have one. This helps the polish to last longer and it smoothes out ridges on the nail surface. Apply two coats of varnish (three if you use frosted varnish), allowing each coat to dry thoroughly before starting the next. Use a long stroke down the centre of the nail first, then do the sides. A top coat will strengthen the varnish, but is not necessary if you are using three coats of frosted varnish. When you apply each layer, remove a hairline edge from each nail tip with the side of your thumb. This will prevent early cracking and splitting.

If you use clear varnish or none at all, moisten a white pencil and run it gently under the nail tips.

When your nails are dry, smooth plenty of hand cream into your skin. Hands that have a tendency to look flushed can be whitened by holding them above your head for a few minutes (a surrender pose!), then massage the fingers, starting at the tips and working gently, but firmly to the base.

Ten Tips to Save Nails in Working Hours

1. Wear rubber cotton-lined gloves when making a fire,

cleaning or washing-up. If you find it difficult to work in gloves, smooth a silicone barrier cream over your hands instead.

2. When using a phone, dial with the end of a pencil or with your knuckle. In an outside call-box keep your gloves on when dialling.

3. If you are a typist keep your nails oval in shape and reasonably short. You might find it a worthwhile investment to buy a set of rubber covers for your typewriter keys.

4. Nails and hobbies do not always go together, so, if you knit, hold your needles with the pads of your fingers and do not let your nails tangle with the wool. Before gardening, dig your nails into a bar of soap, smooth cream into your hands and pop on a pair of gardening gloves. Use a thimble when sewing.

5. Hasty pulling on of a girdle ruins many a nail. Ease yours on between your thumb and forefinger knuckle and keep nails out of the way as much as possible.

6. Use knuckle to press door bells and button clothes (with the help of the thumb).

7. Use pliers to pull out loose nails and drawing pins, and a screwdriver to tighten screws in plugs. Nails were not made for these jobs!

8. Wear gloves when you are out, and don't carry them all the time.

9. Take extra care when using a kitchen grater so that you do not catch a nail in the metal. A thimble worn on thumb and forefinger will prevent accidents.

10. Be careful if your nails have been in hot water. They are softer at this time and carelessness in making a bed or squeezing out wet clothes could ruin a nail.

Ten Pointers towards Lovelier Hands

1. For suppleness, clench fists, then briskly splay out

fingers for two or three minutes, then press fingertips only on a table and lift each finger as high as possible, one at a time.

2. Buy an unflavoured gelatine from a chemist. Take three level teaspoonfuls every day dissolved in fruit juice, hot soup or coffee, to strengthen the nails.

3. Buy a special cream that will remove nicotine, ink, ball-point pen and vegetable stains.

4. A fragrant rose-perfumed lotion from a Paris cosmetic house will ease and sometimes cure, damp clammy hands. It has an astringent, antiseptic action which gives new firmness to the tissues.

5. Do not over-gesticulate with your hands. When sitting, relax them by letting them rest gently in your lap.

6. Keep jars, tubes or bottles of cream in the bathroom, kitchen and desk drawer at the office. Use as much as possible, and always after contact with water and detergents.

7. If you are trying to grow your nails, and one breaks, try the artificial nails which are supplied with a strong adhesive. If your nails break or flake easily, I can recommend a Swiss nail preparation which costs nearly a pound for a tiny bottle, but lasts a year and definitely hardens the weakest nails.

8. Wear a large-domed dress ring if you want to make your hands look slender and more elegant.

9. Make a habit of smoothing cuticle cream around your nails every night. It is a five-minute job which pays almost instant dividends.

10. If your hands are in a very rough condition, thicken cream into them before retiring at night and cover with a pair of loose-fingered cotton gloves.

Your Arms

When caring for your hands do not forget the importance

of a pretty arm too. Rub hand lotion into your elbows after a bath, for smoothness, and use a bleaching cream or half a lemon to ease away redness and keep the skin white.

If your arms are flabby or thin, swimming, rowing, golf and tennis will tone up muscles and build more, if necessary.

Here is a dual purpose exercise that helps both the thin and the flabby arm. Spread arms out, keeping palms open and up. Clench down and back as far as you can, still keeping the arms straight out at each side of you. Do this 20 times a day and you will soon start to feel the muscles tightening.

Your Feet

Have you ever been to a chiropodist? It is surprising how many people, especially teenagers, regard chiropody as something for the older generation, but a qualified chiropodist told me: "A regular visit to a chiropodist is just as important as a dental check-up or as morale-lifting as a manicure during a visit to the hairdresser."

It is worth taking the plunge and making an appointment for a professional pedicure. Fees are reasonable, and usually around ten shillings for a check-up and pedicure. You walk out on air!

Wooden exercise sandals worn in the house, and outdoors in the summer, are excellent for toning weakened foot muscles. Walking barefoot is one of the best foot tonics of all. With your bare feet attempt to pick up a ball of paper with your toes, or sit down, cross your knees and rotate each foot from the ankle 20 times.

Summer or winter it is a good idea to puff some deodorant foot powder into your stockings and shoes, especially if you are on your feet most of the day. In summer, you can prevent blisters by strengthening the skin of your feet with methylated spirits or surgical spirit. Never break a blister purposely. This way lies infection.

Never regard a pedicure as a waste of time. Your feet, although they are covered most of the day, are certainly among the most hardworking parts of your body and as such, they deserve special attention.

Pedicure Plan

Scrub your feet gently first (in the bath is as good a place as any) and use a soapy pumice to smooth away hard patches under the feet or on the heels. Dry well and push the cuticles back and clean under and around the nails with a cotton-wool tipped orange stick dipped in cuticle remover. Trim nails straight across (shaping leads to painful ingrowing nails), and bevel with an emery board. Wash once more, then smooth in a hand cream. If you varnish the nails, place a pad of cotton wool between each toe to facilitate matters.

Leg Show

Give your legs a general tone-up by using a bicycle more often. No bicycle? Then down on to the floor, balance your legs high above your head by resting your elbows on the ground and support your back on your hands. Make a firm cycling motion with your legs.

If your job keeps you on your feet all day, put them up for half an hour when you get home. To counteract swollen legs and feet, lie on the floor with a pillow behind you and rest your legs on the edge of a chair or the bed. It also helps to change your heel height during the day.

Heavy hair growth on legs may be removed by electrical treatment, and a depilatory cream will do for a lighter growth. Fair-skinned people should, in the majority of cases, be able to leave the hair on their legs without touching it as it barely shows. A good cream or body lotion smoothed in will make all legs look more attractive, especially in summer when you are not wearing stockings.

And when all is said and done, remember that legs are for walking. So step out whenever you can. Never catch a bus when you can possibly walk. The more you use your legs in this way, the better will be your general circulation and muscle tone.

9

SKIN CARE

A fully-trained beautician, Hungarian-born Elizabeth Burke, who is in charge of a beauty salon in one of London's new hotels, has this to say about British skins: "You English women are very lucky—you have the best skins in the world, for which you probably have to thank the dampness of your climate!"

However, the most beautiful hothouse flower cannot stay perfect unless it is nourished and well tended. Likewise the skin of your body and your complexion will become dry and lined without attention.

You can counteract the effects of the elements with a pleasant daily routine of cleansing, balancing, toning and protecting. Remove make-up and cleanse your face with a cream or lotion prepared for this purpose. This will remove far more grime from the pores than ordinary soap and will not dry the skin, leaving that taut feeling often associated with a soap wash. Provide balance with a skin care cream appropriate to your needs (anti-wrinkle for the older woman, moisturisers for everyone reaching the 25-year mark and over, astringents to tighten oily skins) and tone with massage, using the first and middle finger knuckles to "step" out firmly upwards over your face. A final tone is provided with astringents and tonic waters or fresheners. Finally, protect your complexion with a foundation cream and powder.

Many of us tend to think that the skin is only surface thin, but in reality it is a quarter of an inch thick, and is a thriving combination of glands, pores and tissues.

Walking and other forms of exercise all help to improve a general skin tone.

A dry friction bath is invaluable for keeping skin pores healthy and active. Take a fairly rough towel and rub it well all over your body, not forgetting arms, wrists, chest, back and feet. A loofah bath will provide a similar result. See that your bath water is just warm enough, pour in some oil, then rub the loofah over your body until you feel tingling and alive all over. First thing in the morning is an ideal time for this, as it sets you up for the rest of the day.

Recognise Your Skin Type

If you are to take advantage of the many cosmetics on the market today, you should know your skin type, otherwise you may buy an unsuitable preparation. Here then, for your personal guidance, are the four main categories.

Normal Skin. This is usually clear and near perfect. Smooth and even textured, it has no shiny spots and rarely develops blackheads.

Dry Skin. This feels taut after washing, especially if soap is used, and tends to go dry and flaky in wind, sun and rough weather. It needs daily treatment in order to ward off premature lines.

Oily Skin. This is recognisable by shiny patches around the nose, on the chin and forehead. Pores are often enlarged and there maybe a sallow appearance with a tendency towards blackheads and pimples, particularly among teenagers.

Combination Skin. This is a blend of the dry and oily. The oily parts are found around the nose, forehead and chin, and the cheeks are dry.

Once you know your type, you should keep to an appropriate beauty routine that will enable you to make the very best of yourself.

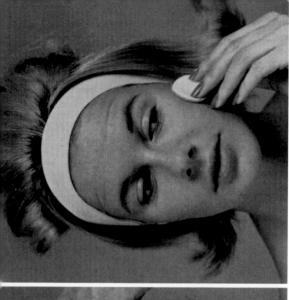

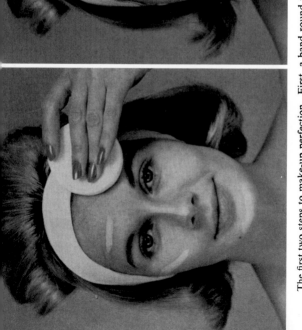

The first two steps to make-up perfection. First, a band round the hair to keep it free of powder, then a gentle but thorough cleansing prior to application of foundation lotion. Secondly, a touch of rouge if necessary, followed by a light film of powder to provide a matt finish.

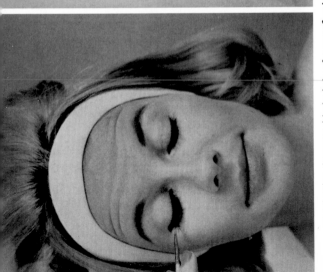

Highlighting the eyes with the help of a superfine brush and mascara is followed by the final touch in achieving make-up perfection. The lips should be neatly outlined with a lip-liner and then filled in with a clear lipstick.

Normal Skin needs cleansing with a soft complexion milk or a special soap-cream, followed by the application of a skin freshener and a moisturiser, before using tinted foundation and powder. Once or twice a week use a conditioning cream to maintain texture and elasticity.

Dry Skin. Cleanse with a cold cream or a cleansing cream and stimulate with a tonic water or a freshener. Add a moisture balancer prior to your foundation cream, and every night massage in an emollient, conditioner or other nourishing cream. A tissue oil may also prove beneficial if used around the eyes, nose and throat at night.

Oily Skin. Remove make-up with a cleansing milk, and counteract greasiness with an astringent lotion. Use a moisture balance prepared for oily skins under your foundation. Once or twice a week apply a conditioning cream. Cleanse at night with a good soap-cream.

Combination Skin. Use a cleansing milk first, and tone up the cheeks with a freshener. Use an astringent lotion on the oily sections only, before applying make-up. A vitamin cream should be used on the dry areas every night, and only once or twice a week on the oily.

All these routines may be carried out in a minimum of time.

Skin Problems

Broken Veins. Wash with lukewarm water and avoid extremes of hot and cold. Protect your skin daily with a light foundation. You might also invest in a cream that is supercharged with special biological extracts which reconstitute and stimulate skin cells.

Acne. Always consult a doctor or dermatologist and they will prescribe treatment which will almost certainly include a diet which cuts out rich food. Apply an anti-acne lotion morning and night for alleviation.

Blackheads and Whiteheads. If these are persistent, see a dermatologist. Use cleansing grains (obtainable at your chemist or local beauty counter) and appropriate face masks. A dab of surgical spirit is advisable on the trouble-spots. Always be sure that your hands are spotlessly clean before touching your face, a and keep medicated blemish eraser stick or cream handy to camouflage spots under your make-up.

Sallow Skin. This can be considerably remedied with face masks, and daily patting with a freshener to stimulate circulation and provide a healthier colouring.

Large or Open Pores. The use of masks and astringents, after cleansing with pore grains, will help to refine enlarged pores. Use a light foundation only. Anything heavy will clog the pores.

Know Your Cosmetics

No one could blame any woman if she feels confused when faced with an array of beauty preparations. The following explanatory list may assist you when you make your next choice.

Anti-acne cream or lotion reduces excessive oily secretions associated with this problem.

Anti-wrinkle creams put life into dry skin and help to reduce and prevent lines.

Astringents freshen and tighten oily skins.

Cleansing milk and cream remove traces of make-up without removing skin's moisture.

Cold cream is deep cleansing, smooths and softens the skin. Especially suitable for dry skins.

Conditioners do what they say, condition the general tone of the skin.

Contour-lifting lotions control the sag of older skin and provide lift and firmness. Very effective.

Emollients return texture and smoothness to dry and

wrinkled skin. Also provide a protective and lubricating action.

Hormone creams work beneath the skin surface, filling out skin tissues.

Moisturisers retain the balance of moisture in the skin and may be worn under make-up. There are varieties for both dry and oily skins.

Muscle oils strengthen weak muscles and tissues, especially around the eyes.

Nourishing creams smooth and lubricate the skin. Especially good for dry skins.

Placenta creams are rejuvenating treatments in themselves, and are for use by the older woman.

Pore grains are suitable for cleansing oily skins which are prone to enlarged pores and blackheads. Very good for teenagers.

Tonic and freshener lotions are refreshing and soothing. They tone up the skin and help to provide a good natural colour.

Vitamin creams are extra nourishing. They assist healing in many cases.

Ten Steps to Complexion Beauty

1. Drink plenty of water, and eat as much fresh fruit and raw vegetable as you can. If you have a liquidiser in your home, drink fruit and vegetable cocktails daily as these are unsurpassed for cleansing the blood-stream naturally. Make sure that you get plenty of protein (eggs, fish, milk, cheese and meat), Vitamin C (oranges, rosehips, parsley, blackcurrants) and Vitamin E (butter).

2. Take *fresh* lemon juice every morning in warm water, unsweetened if possible.

3. Use an all-in-one deodorant soap at bath times to nourish your skin and keep it fresh.

4. Try a face mask every so often (oatmeal is good) to brighten your skin thoroughly.

5. Smooth a body lotion all over your skin after a bath, to give you top-to-toe smoothness.

6. Guard against baths that are too hot, as you may cause broken veins on your thighs, which can be unsightly in a bathing costume or tennis shorts.

7. If, by chance, you do not wear make-up, remember that you should still protect your skin with an invisible layer of moisturiser in the day, and a conditioner at night.

8. A sun lamp works wonders by providing you with a year-round tan, and it helps to clear blemishes. *Always* follow the manufacturer's directions implicitly, and *never* sit before a lamp longer than the specified time.

9. Consider a short session of exercises every morning to stimulate your circulation and remove any trace of a facial pallor.

10. Take a Turkish bath once in a while. You will be amazed at the grime that leaves the skin you originally thought so clean!

Incidentally, many women do not like using cosmetics containing animal tissue fats. If this happens in your case, you will find a wide range of creams, lotions and cosmetics at health stores which are made purely from herbs, vegetable oils and fruits. They can all be obtained by post if there is no health store in your district.

10

GOOD IMPRESSIONS

Relaxation

Beauty, calmness and serenity should be inseparable. Unfortunately, life speeds on at such a pace today that many women, young and old alike, are swept up in a routine rush of home to office travel. Many, too, combine home-making and the care of children with a job. Sooner or later they are bound to feel stress.

Relaxation should never be considered a waste of time. On the contrary, a ten minute cat-nap taken by a house-wife after lunch, or mid-morning, will enable her to get through her work much faster afterwards. Once a week all women should treat themselves to a soothing beauty routine. This will often work more wonders than an evening in a smoky coffee bar or at the cinema.

There are many ways of relaxing. Here are just a few of them.

Take a leisurely, repeat l-e-i-s-u-r-e-l-y bath, scented with pine essence or perfumed oil or salts. Have a foam cushion at your neck (buy one cheaply at a chain store and cover it with plastic material), and forget work for a while. If you are a housewife, try taking a bath during the day and see how much better you feel.

Go for a walk every day, either first thing in the morning, at midday or last thing at night.

Visit your library and re-discover the pleasure of reading. Relax over a cup of coffee and some conversation after your evening meal, *before* you start washing up.

In bed, both night and morning, s-t-r-e-t-c-h like a prize contented cat until you tingle throughout and every muscle feels eased.

Count ten before shouting at someone, or before plunging into an argument that you know will lead you nowhere. If you have had a heated argument with someone, try saying sorry, and mean it, and see how much more relaxed you feel as a result.

Learn to take a more genial and tolerant view of life. Remember, it isn't really a disaster if a meal is a few minutes late, or a neighbour visits you when you are in the middle of the weekly wash!

Sleep, of course, is the most important form of complete relaxation. A lukewarm bath, a warm sweet drink or the gentle routine of brushing hair or manicuring nails, all help to relax you before you retire to bed. A light spray of perfume on your pillow also helps.

If you cannot sleep, then see your doctor. But in any case, remember that just lying there in the dark helps to refresh and rest your body.

Sir John Barbirolli, the famous conductor, told me: "I never have more than four or five hours of sleep at night. But I don't worry. Instead, I lie there and think of all the peace I should be missing if I were asleep!"

All About Glamour

"Glamour," says the dictionary, is "magic, enchantment, delusive or alluring beauty." In everyday terms glamour is also an art, a skill and a business that fascinates a man.

Have you ever heard the story of the painter who came to London and asked a stranger how to get to the National Gallery? "Practise!" replied the stranger, "Practise!"

And if you want glamour, follow that self-same advice and, practise!

86

Glamour has many facets. It is: a white mohair dress with a crystal brooch; something in chiffon with a sparkle of gold or silver; something pink, a hat or a soft woolly dress; something gold like a loose shimmering hip-length blouse in brocade or lamé, and worn over a scarlet chiffon skirt.

It is: grey or white fur, fake or real, around the neck; an evening headscarf made out of a square of the palest blue, pink or white organza, with a small posy of artificial lily-of-the-valley tucked under the chin; slim long pants in dusky blue or pink velvet; a wide halo of a hat in lemon, white or shiny black straw; a silky shirtwaister dress, cinched at the waist, and the neck filled in with a pile of tiny immitation pearls or glass seedbeads.

It is: a velvet bow at the side or back of well groomed hair; links of pearly beads, plus one rope of beads the colour of your dress, wound around your wrist instead of your neck; a creamy petticoat edged with snuff brown lace; pure simplicity in the form of a black dress with no jewellery other than crystal or pearl drop ear-rings; inexpensive pretty extras in a handbag, such as a gold-backed note-book and pencil.

Glamour is being groomed, vital and confident, and proud of being a woman. It is a self-knowledge, and it can all be yours, with practice.

Fifty Pathways to Good Grooming

1. Wind transparent sticky tape around your hand, sticky side outwards, and use it to pick up fluff and hairs from a black dress.

2. Spring-clean your handbag every week and keep it clinically tidy with a neat plastic bag to hold make-up.

3. Don't wear a garment immediately after pressing. Give it plenty of time to air and dry first, otherwise it will crease easily.

4. Keep suits, dresses and blouses fresh with underarm shields, and wash them frequently.

5. Give shoes a rub with the duster after each wearing, and polish regularly.

6. Always have an extra pair of stockings handy in your desk drawer or bedroom, ready for an emergency.

7. Wash your powder puff often. Renew it regularly.

8. Stitch up broken straps, petticoats, waistbands, etc. as soon as possible.

9. Keep white gloves white by washing after each wearing.

10. Clear out lipstick stubs ruthlessly and those almost empty nail varnish bottles which have a habit of mounting up.

11. Sponge the inside of a suit collar or coat and keep it free of make-up.

12. At the end of the summer put away your summer dresses washed, starched and clean, ready for a possible early heat-wave the following year!

13. At the end of winter, dry-clean coats and suits, put boots away in a cleaned and repaired condition.

14. If you are a housewife keep a small box of touch-up cosmetics in the kitchen. The breadman is just as appreciative of good looks as your husband and hairdresser.

15. Keep an eye on shoe heels. Never leave them until they are right down, otherwise they may be difficult to repair effectively.

16. Make sure that your hems are straight, and the stitching is intact.

17. Always carry a small clothes brush in your handbag.

18. See that all hooks and eyes are fixed and firm.

19. Do not iron velvet. Hang it in a steamy bathroom instead to remove creases.

20. Do not dry sweaters on unpadded hangers. They will leave a mark on the material.

21. If you are not absolutely sure and happy when buying a garment, then don't!

22. Wash hairbrush and comb every time you shampoo your hair.

23. Do not let your finger nails grow into talons. Keep them a reasonable length.

24. Brush suits and place on hangers immediately after wearing.

25. Remember that a visit to the dry cleaner is often cheaper than buying a new outfit!

26. Always look at your rear view in a mirror before going out and brush your shoulders.

27. Make sure that you are always pleasant to be near. Check that you are using the correct deodorant and anti-perspirant.

28. Throw away old laddered nylons, and keep fresh ones in a box.

29. Dip cottons, blouses and scarves in a light liquid ready-made starch to keep them fresh.

30. Remove ink stains from fabric by soaking or sponging in warm suds, then launder. If the stain has been in for some time, dip stained white fabrics in cold water, spread with salt and squeeze on lemon juice. Leave for an hour, then rinse thoroughly and launder. Coloured fabrics can be soaked in milk or treated with permanganate of potash ($\frac{1}{2}$ teaspoonful to a pint of water), then rinse, and launder washable fabrics in a soapless detergent.

31. To remove ball-point pen marks, sponge with methylated spirit or carbon tetrachloride. Drip cleaner on to the stain, and when ink has dissolved rub the mark with a cloth dipped in the cleaner. Always test rayons and man-made fabrics before using methylated spirits.

32. If you wear white or light gloves often, always keep a spare pair handy in case you do not have time to launder them.

33. After a sea bathe rinse your swimsuit in fresh water to remove traces of salt which will spoil the elasticity.

34. Make sure that suits fit perfectly around the front and back of the shoulders when you buy and wear them.

35. When travelling, pack lingerie, stockings, sweaters, shoes, etc. in separate plastic bags for tidiness and ease of packing.

36. Pack pleated skirts by rolling and pulling through an old stocking, which has had the foot removed.

37. Hang skirts and slacks on individual hangers. Never double skirts or hang by loops, as they will lose shape.

38. Keep shopping bags and baskets clean and in good repair. They are just as important in their own way as a handbag.

39. Try to keep one day and one evening outfit ready for a sudden invitation. If possible, keep appropriate shoes, gloves and handbag etc. on hand, to save last minute accessory searches.

40. Keep sweaters lightly folded in plastic bags. When you wash a sweater squeeze lightly if it is wool and never wring hard. The best way is to pat out excess moisture by rolling it in a towel.

41. Do not hoard old shoes, dresses, etc., which you have not worn for a very long time. A charitable organisation could make better use of them, and your wardrobe will become freer.

42. Never go out with badly chipped nail varnish. Better to go out with none at all if you have no time to do your nails properly.

43. Wear a silk or rayon scarf inside the collar of a suède jacket to prevent it from catching make-up marks.

44. Think twice before buying a cheap handbag or pair

of gloves. A more expensive choice which is better made, will pay dividends not only in length of life, but to your morale.

45. Do not carry a cheap plastic bag with an expensive dress or suit. The effect will be ruined. Far better to buy a less expensive dress and have good accessories.

46. Always have clean hands, nails and teeth when you go out.

47. Do not wear all your jewellery at once. One good brooch or ring looks far more effective than a charm bracelet, ear-rings, a jazzy brooch and a necklace all worn together.

48. Keep all lingerie scrupulously fresh with regular washing.

49. Save used open perfume bottles to pop into your drawers to leave a lingering fragrance among your clothes.

50. Grooming begins at home, so keep all your cosmetics and drawers tidy. Try linking necklaces on to hooks inside your wardrobe door, and do not leave powder all over the dressing table.

Mannerisms for Beauty

1. Hold a telephone gracefully and don't clench it. Put a smile into your voice.

2. To remove a coat or jacket attractively, undo the buttons from the top and gently drop the garment off your shoulders, easing arms from sleeves. Don't tug at sleeves.

3. When removing gloves, ease each finger off in turn.

4. Take a tip from stage actresses when sitting down, and keep legs together and arrange to one side with the feet slightly crossed.

5. When making an entrance into a crowded room, relax, take a good breath, walk in slowly and look around for your host or hostess.

6. When sitting, don't slump into your chair. Relax and keep your posture erect and graceful.

7. Practise resting your hands gently in your lap and don't clench them tightly.

8. When you are being escorted by a man give him a chance to open a door, pull out a chair for you or help you off with your coat.

11

THE COVER-UP STORY

How to Buy Clothes

Alexander Plunkett Greene, the tall, astute partner of one of Britain's top fashion designers, Mary Quant, gave me this advice: "Dress to please yourself, not the man. If you feel marvellous in an outfit and a boyfriend doesn't like it, change the boyfriend!"

To which Mary Quant herself added: "Never go shopping for clothes with your best friend, it's fatal!"

John Cavanagh, the man who designed Princess Alexandra's wedding dress, believes that a dress should always enhance the personality of its wearer. It should never be bought with the intention of matching the eyes, but should blend with a woman's general colouring.

All very sound advice, and I would add: always shop for your clothes in a cheerful frame of mind, and never buy in a hurry, otherwise you will find your wardrobe cluttered with clothes that have no real purpose and lack co-ordination with each other.

Ask yourself: "Do I really need it? Will it *do* something for me?" Bear in mind that it is always better to spend your money on one really good suit, dress or coat in a colour and style calculated to get the most out of your accessories and life, than a cheap one which will date quickly and show signs of wear after its first trip to the dry cleaner.

Don't be tempted to buy clothes haphazardly at a sale. Cheap buys are not good buys unless you really need them.

If you are not completely sure about a garment, it is better to leave it. Try not to be intimidated into buying something by an effusive saleswoman in a fitting cubicle. You are under no obligation.

Have a look at yourself in a full-length mirror outside a cubicle so that you can see yourself in proper perspective. Make sure that shoulders fit without pulling. Jacket and dress tops should be unrumpled and smooth, especially in the space between lapel and arm-hole seam. See that sleeves are long enough, and if they are wide and flappy around the wrist or elbow, it pays to have them elegantly tapered, otherwise they may look dowdy. Collars should fit perfectly, especially when fastened in the front.

Double check the hem and waistlines. If the former is too long or the latter too big, have them altered. If you are buying a suit, it is a good idea to ask the fitter to insert small weights in the jacket hem if the material is light-weight, so that it will hang well.

Try skirts for fit by sitting in them. They should fit easily and not pull over thighs and hips.

Chanel, the French fashion designer who is almost a legend in her lifetime, believes that clothes are made to be worn. "I make fashions," she says, "women can live in, breathe in, feel comfortable in, look younger in." And this is how *you* should feel when buying a new outfit.

"Flattery is of foremost importance in clothes," said Mrs. Margaret Lenz, a handsome Austrian-born woman who is behind one of Britain's major dress firms. She also believes in interpreting fashion rather than following it like a slave. You would do well to follow her example.

Tall, Short, Thin and Plump

TALL WOMEN SHOULD BEWARE of flat heels; accessories

such as handbags and necklaces which are over-large and clumsy, rather than plain handsome; long sleeves that are not long enough; skirts ditto; skirts that are too full (unless they are for evening wear); outsize fabric designs; "shouting" colours; jangly bracelets; men's watches; fussy clothes and sleeveless dresses.

A tall girl should go for the happy medium. Large necklaces, Large handbags and Large this that and the other often make a tall girl unnecessarily conspicuous and unfeminine.

TALL WOMEN SHOULD WEAR shaped and flared skirts to show off their legs; fitted, elbow length and mid-arm length sleeves; three-quarter gloves; shirt-waisters in all fabrics from cotton and silk to velvet; sleek jackets in stiffened slub silk or bouclé tweed; soft bulky sweaters; cowl and turtle necklines; Chanel-type suits; pencil-skirted dresses with bloused or battle-dress tops; three-quarter coats and toning skirts; medium-high heels; wide brimmed hats; wool or nylon pilecoats (unless you are bosomy) and plenty of mohairs and thick-knit woollens. For evening wear anything goes from a Grecian or Empire line to a crinoline.

SHORT WOMEN SHOULD BEWARE of wide-brimmed hats; wide belts; large-patterned fabrics; over-high heels and hats (they knock your balance for six); large portmanteau handbags; very full skirts; chunky jackets; three-quarter coats; fussy hats; too many frills, wide or high collars.

SHORT WOMEN SHOULD WEAR V-necklines; princess and Empire lines; sleeveless dresses (but only if arms are slender); neat shifts in plain fabrics; tailored sheath dresses; head-hugging cloche styled hats; one colour combinations in separates; beltless dresses; neat, un-cluttered jewellery; plain shoes.

Small women usually want to look taller, and the

appearance of extra inches can be given by choosing clothes that carry the line up in an unbroken vertical. Anything which breaks it, such as a sash or wide collar, immediately cuts off those "inches."

THIN WOMEN SHOULD BEWARE OF tight and skimpy clothes; pencil-slim dresses in black or any other dark colour; sleeveless dresses; very low necklines; vertical striped fabrics; fitted sweaters; sleeves that are not long enough; over-fitted suits.

THIN WOMEN SHOULD WEAR pastel colours—soft dusky pinks and blues, stone and milk chocolate browns; soft grape juice greens; thick cuddly fabrics such as mohairs; soft fine wool fabrics with skirts backed in vylene; horizontal patterns; chunky sweaters; two-tone colour combinations, such as a red jacket and dark green slacks; or a dark green skirt and a paler green sweater, to give the impression of more width and body; boxy jackets; Chanel-style suits (they suit almost every figure type); battle-dress and blazer jackets and tops; full, hip-line blouses; bell-shaped or flared skirts; wide-collared coats; frilly-fronted blouses.

If you are thin around the bosom, don't be afraid to wear a padded bra which will boost your morale and make your clothes look so much better.

PLUMP WOMEN SHOULD BEWARE OF the majority of the items listed for the short woman, plus slacks; fluffy sweaters; and fussy jewellery.

PLUMP WOMEN SHOULD WEAR semi-tailored coats; those Chanel suits (useful for smoothing out the bulges); one piece, beltless dresses; perfectly fitting slim skirts; long tapered sleeves; medium to dark colours, but including subtle bright ones; bias cut skirts.

Whatever your size, understate your clothes and accessories rather than the opposite. Elegance and simplicity always go hand in hand.

Lady Isobel Barnett.

Lady Mavis Pilkington.

Town and Country

If you are faced with regular trips between town and country choose a suit in a fine check or pretty bouclé tweed. Both will fit into the country scene with the addition of a warm sweater and string-back gloves, and will translate into city-goers with plain kid gloves, handbag and silk shirt. This is certainly your best plan if you want a suit for town and country and cannot afford two.

For city wear only, steer clear of full skirts (they have a habit of blowing up in busy streets on gusty days); fussiness and too many colours at once. Place the accent on simple suits, speedily washed blouses (silk is a glamour winner); coat dresses, linen summer dresses, tailored coats and uncrushable, uncreasable fabrics. Clean gloves should always be worn. A hat is not an essential, except for formal occasions, if your hair is cut well enough to remain smart and tidy.

In the country there is no need to fall into the old-fashioned "tweedy" trap with masculine suits and plainer than plain twinsets. Instead, step out in gay bulk sweaters and slacks or knickerbockers; bright leather jackets; plaids and bouclés, and choose mellow russets, reds, golds and greens.

Summer Days and Nights

For office hours choose cool cucumbers, pinks, greys and lilacs and all shades of blue. Buy or make loose-topped dresses with plenty of room around the arm seams. Wear cotton undies which are cooler than nylon and always have spotless cream or white gloves. Summer evenings call for the fresh crispness of organza stitched over a flowered glazed cotton, or silky bright pants and loose shirts. Beware of sloppy, shapeless cardigans. If you must wear one choose a tailored design banded with a material to match your dress.

Winter Wear

In the winter, think *colour*. Don't buy a dark coat because it "won't show the dirt." It will collect grime just as much as a bright red or green, and will still have to be cleaned. If you want an all-purpose coat try a pure wool or nylon "fur" pile coat which is warm during the day, and attractive over an evening dress at night.

Long skirts, worn over gay tights, are prettier than slacks for winter evenings at home.

If you are faced with a number of dances and only want one dress, make a basic, full length, strapless dress in satin or similar fabric, then alter its looks with a long contrasting satin stole, a dark velvet over-jacket, a short satin bolero in a contrasting shade, a band of white fur or a frill of puffed lace around the bodice top, or a complete overdress Eastern style which slits up to the armpits and ties with small bows there, and on the shoulders.

A Flair for Colour

Many women are timid when it comes to colour. The same shades are chosen year after year because they are considered "safe." But almost any colour goes these days, because the wide range of hair and cosmetic shades enables you to tone your colouring at will. The many colour combinations which were once considered taboo, lilac and orange and pink and scarlet, for instance, are very popular with fabric designers and look stunning if worn with handsome neutral accessories.

For general wear choose colours that flatter your skin, your eyes and your personality and make you feel really confident. There is no need to be a slave to fashion colours if they don't suit your temperament. Remember, many of these annual fashion colour changes are nothing more than a stimulus planned by industry to induce women to spend more and buy more in the clothing and shoe shops.

If you want to try a new colour combination, but are not too sure what to choose, think of nature's blends and you won't go far wrong. Brunette? Then how about a striking tangerine-coloured coat with pith cream accessories? Fair? Try hyacinth blue and green. Grey haired? Choose a rich aubergine with cream or black accessories for daytime, and sweetpea shades at night.

There are only two points to bear in mind in the colour game. If you are young you can be daring, but after 35 veer towards the more subtle blends.

The All-in-One Outfit

However large or small your wardrobe, do try to have one outfit that will take you virtually anywhere.

A brief-sleeved or elbow length, simply styled dress with a bell or pencil skirt, and a semi-fitted jacket is ideal. For material choose a heavy stiff slubbed silk; a fine bouclé tweed or good tailored jersey. Take your colour pick from black, pine green, midnight blue or olive and keep to plain black or neutral accessories. Patent shoes and handbag are pretty and will take you through a day into an evening. For jewellery keep to one good piece, such as a cluster brooch.

12

ACCESSORIES TO THE FACT

Give three women the same dress and one will look stunning, the second uninspired and the third nondescript. The major difference lies in their choice of accessories. Well chosen, they will transform an inexpensive outfit into the model range, and if they are wrong an exclusive dress will look ordinary.

Pay as much as you can for accessories and keep to plain, well-styled articles. When shopping for them take a small piece of material from the seam of your outfit to ensure a perfect blend or contrast. If ever in doubt keep to the blacks, neutrals and browns, and never be tempted to match everything. It is always more effective to have one accessory, your hat, for example, in a different colour to your shoes, gloves and handbag.

Former leading model and fashion advisor to the B.B.C., Miss Shelagh Wilson, now Mrs. Charles Parnell, has three sets of basic accessories in brown, black and putty. "They go with everything," she explained. "Always keep accessories simple and well organised. The best dressed girl I know is a Mexican who plans her outfits down to the very last detail. No impulsive buying for her."

Hat Tricks

Hats come an easy second to well-groomed hair in the glamour stakes, *if* they are chosen with care and thought. They should flatter and soften your face, especially if you are older, and, if anything, should always make you look a little younger.

A light-coloured hat, a halo of white, a pastel of pink or blue, works wonders with most faces because it reflects a becoming light on to the skin.

Here, from the Millinery Institute of Great Britain, are ten tips for every girl and woman, who wants to look her best in a hat.

1. If you're the angular type, be sure to keep away from tall, narrow styles.

2. Frivolous looking hats should be out for the full-figured girl, as they draw attention to Nature's "over-generosity." Medium-sized shapes, with the accent on line and brim are best.

3. Teenagers should keep away from sophisticated hats, as they look best in simple, off-the-face styles.

4. Wearing tweeds? Then plain sporty felts are the thing.

5. Spectacle frames should either echo or tone in with the colouring of an ensemble.

6. If you have a long nose, minimise it by wearing a hat with a forward crown.

7. Small hats with neat brims and elaborate hats may be worn with inconspicuous spectacles.

8. A heart-shaped face calls for a deep on-the-brow hat.

9. Hats in contrasting colour to the rest of your clothes usually give an illusion of being short.

10. Conversely, a dark hat and dress will make you look taller.

Toeing the Line

According to the Queen's shoemaker, Edward Rayne: "The wrong pair of shoes can ruin the most elegant clothes. As accessories they are as important as hats, but there are many women who buy clothes which suit them and then buy haphazardly the shoes to wear with them.

"Black shoes are an essential part of a woman's shoe wardrobe, but apart from this the colours of the shoes depend entirely on the clothes with which they are to be worn. I consider that a woman should have a shoe wardrobe in exactly the same way as she has a clothes wardrobe. It should contain shoes for every occasion, which, at a minimum, includes day shoes for town, day shoes for the country, dressier afternoon or early cocktail time shoes and evening shoes.

"The wardrobe can and should be extended beyond this, however, for it is false economy to buy one pair of shoes and wear them day after day until they wear out. Any well-dressed woman who can afford it, should have ten pairs of shoes in her wardrobe and she will find that they will last her a long time, if she has them repaired regularly.

"Before buying new shoes, a woman should think very carefully for what purpose she needs them. In logical sequence, a woman buying new shoes should decide how much she can afford, plan with what clothes she will wear the shoes and whether they complement the other shoes she already has.

"Finally, if she has time, she should go to two or three shops before making a final choice."

It is also a good idea to buy shoes when you have been out for an hour or two, so that your feet will have had time to expand. If a pair is comfortable then, it always will be.

Take care of your shoes by inserting frames into them at night, and if they should be wet stuff them firmly with newspaper and leave in a warmish place, but not directly in front of a heat source.

Undercover Story

Never in the history of costume has a woman had such an array of pretty underwear to choose from, and at such budget-conscious prices. Chain stores particularly have a tremendous array of everything from bras and slips to housecoats and négligées. Colour-wise you can have everything from traditional white to scarlet, snuff brown, aquamarine and navy. A number of lingerie organisations have joined forces with foundation manufacturers to produce garments that will match.

A basic lingerie wardrobe should include the foundation garments mentioned in Chapter 3, under the heading "Foundation Facts," plus four slips (two light and two dark); a warm wool or quilted dressing gown; a cotton or nylon dressing gown and a pretty bedjacket.

If possible, wash lingerie daily, taking special notice of straps and hems. Use hand-hot suds for cotton, nylon and terylene, and warm suds for acetate, tricel and silk. Foundation garments should be washed weekly, and bras two or three times a week. Treat extra soiled parts with a soft sudsy brush and rinse well. Drip dry bras, and roll girdles and corsets in a towel before hanging over a line to dry.

The Magic of Perfume

I am purposely devoting a little more space to this accessory because it is the most alluring of all. In spite of this, the Society of French Perfumers tell me that only 32·5 per cent of the women of Great Britain use perfume regularly, compared with 86 per cent in America and an even greater number in France.

Perfumes, like wines, have taken many decades to perfect. Both come from the fruits of the earth, and both, as William Locke once said, "are great looseners of human sympathy."

Interviewed early one morning, before she rose in fact, film star Natalie Wood was recorded as saying: "Perfume, perfume first before anything. I love it." Rudyard Kipling admitted: "Smells are surer than sounds or sights to make your heart-strings crack."

Even today there is an exotic air about perfume-making that progress has not diminished. In France, home of the world's finest perfumes, mountainous piles of blossoms are waiting in the great halls of the perfume manufacturers of Provence, all ready to go into the "pot."

It was an Arabian doctor called Avicenna who invented the art of extracting the fragrance of plants and flowers by distillation in the tenth century. Before this they had only used scented resins and spices and never thought of employing chemistry. Perfume sprang into commercial existence in France in 1190, but it was Louis XIV who established it as a master trade.

The creation of perfume is like composing music—it has so many "notes," but writing a symphony would be simple in comparison. It takes seven years of testing to perfect a new perfume from the time of gathering the flowers. There are 4,000 raw materials from all over the world from which to choose, and only the best ingredients are used. One of them, jasmine, may cost as much as £40 for an ounce. Experts explain that perfume is like a body, with a head or the top note, the intrinsic character which is the heart, and the background which is the body.

Choosing Your Perfume

Keep an open mind when buying new perfume. Do not copy someone else's before trying it on yourself for at least thirty minutes. Every scent has a different reaction on different people according to the acidity of the skin. Buy a small bottle first; in fact it is always a good idea to buy small and often. A large flagon looks attractive on the dressing-table, but the perfume evaporates with time and loses its strength in light and air. So keep your perfume in the dark, and well-stoppered.

A good perfume should last three to four hours. To get the most out of it dab it on the pulse spots, where your warm blood will act as a diffuser; the nape of the neck, the wrist, behind the knees, in the crook of the arms, even the ankles. Complete its effect by using a matching bath oil and toilet water.

Never be hurried in your selection. This perfume is going to be your signature tune, and the man in your mind is going to think of you in association with it.

Some stores list perfumes like wine lists in their catalogues, with a write-up of their particular bouquet, which at once stimulates sales and helps choice. To a woman a knowledge of good perfume is as important as the names and nuances of wine are to a man, and part of her elegance.

Never try more than about three perfumes at the same time, as their scents will mingle and you will not get a true perfume. Dab some inside your wrist, leave it for a moment (all perfumes react in a different way on different skins) then inhale. Try a second choice on your other wrist, and a third in the crook of your arm.

Perfume Groups
Perfumes are divided into various groups which are described here, together with some typical examples.

Floral. Magical, flowery blends, e.g. Quelque Fleurs, Detchema, Joy, Le Dix, Fleurs de Rocaille, No. 5, L'Aimant, Sortilège, Chant d'Aromes, Arpège, Nuit de Longchamp, Le Dandy, Je Reviens, Capricci.

Fruits. Warm, pungent and mature scents, e.g. Femme, Tendres Nuits.

Spicy. Warm, modern scents, e.g. Jolie Madame, Cabochard, Chantilly, Coup de Feu, Pêle-Mêle.

Woody. Evocative perfumes, often with a rich, smooth warmth about them, e.g. L'Interdit, Crèpe de Chine, Heure Intime, Tiara, Vent Vert.

Jewellery

This is the final sparkle in an ensemble, and it is worth remembering that good fake jewellery can often be as attractive as the real thing. Large cluster rings, for instance, are well within the reach of any woman today, whereas the real gem group is a once-in-a-lifetime buy.

It is important to bear in mind the colour of your eyes when choosing jewels, especially real ones, so remember this when choosing an engagement ring which will be with you all your life.

Gems in shades of red, yellow, brown and coral are becoming to brown-eyed brunettes; blue-eyed brunettes should choose from sapphires, diamonds, turquoise and aquamarine. Blondes with blue eyes suit turquoise, lapis lazuli, sapphires, aquamarines and amethyst. Grey and light hazel eyes are given added beauty if moonstones, aquamarines and topaz are worn. Redheads look best with emeralds and zircons which reflect the green lights of their eyes. Diamonds, needless to say, are universally becoming.

Rings on Your Fingers

Here is the advice of Mr. E. Hodges, director of Garrards, the Royal Jewellers: "Hands have personality, so choose a ring to flatter them. An oval or rectangular ring 'slims' short fingers and broad hands by taking the eye down the finger. Girls with tiny, delicate hands, need small rings with smallish stones, or a single, bigger stone, in an extremely simple setting. Big square, or rectangular rings, tend to look ostentatious and swamp a small hand. Slim fingered girls have no worries at all. They can wear large dramatic rings with large square-cut and oval stones, and exotic styles, to perfection."

The Right Size

There is now a device which can be incorporated into the shank of a ring to enlarge it. This is especially useful to any woman with an enlarged knuckle, since the ring can be slipped over and then closed firmly. It is also useful for the housewife whose fingers tend to swell with housekeeping chores or for arthritic hands. Virtually invisible, it costs a few extra pounds, but is well worth it.

Jewel Care

Mr. Hodges recommends that good jewellery be examined regularly to check on settings, clasps and threading, rather than risk the loss of a precious or semi-precious stone, and he gives the following tips for jewel care:

Keep jewellery out of the kitchen, away from steam and heat which may affect paste in costume jewellery. Store each piece separately in tiny chamois bags and keep out of your handbag, which is usually dusty from face powder which can cause miniature erosion on jewellery. The only time it is acceptable to keep jewellery in your handbag is when you are out or away and then it should be wrapped in a clean hanky.

Amber. Like pearls, amber needs to be kept apart from other jewellery as its surface is easily scratched. All that is needed to keep it clean and in good condition is careful polishing with a soft cloth. If it has been so neglected that it has become encrusted, a paste made of fine pumice powder mixed with water can be used to clear the surface, with a final polishing with a soft clean cloth.

Coral. Clean by a careful washing in warm soapy water, rinse, dry, and then polish with a chamois cloth.

Cornelian. Same as coral.

Costume jewellery. Stones in costume jewellery are usually pasted in so that putting them in very hot water might dissolve the paste. Soap and lukewarm water is the rule here. An old toothbrush is useful in removing dirt from cracks of elaborate pieces, but beware of loosening the stones.

Diamonds and precious gemstones. The beauty of precious stones depends on the freedom of light reflections and refraction through the stone. This can be noticeably dimmed if the underside of the gem is not completely clean. Soapsuds, often to blame for dingy appearance, can be removed by careful brushing with a small hog's brush dipped in surgical spirit. The backs of gems and settings should be most carefully cleaned with this, followed by careful washing of the jewels in hot water. Dry carefully afterwards with a soft complexion brush. Never clean corners with a pointed implement.

Pearls. These should not be washed as the surface is absorbent. Any film that clings to pearls should be removed by wiping over gently with a chamois leather. It is most important to keep pearls away from perfume and to keep them in a box on their own.

Silver jewellery. If badly tarnished it can be dipped in a silver-dip solution, left for about 10 seconds, rinsed in hot water and then dried with the specially impregnated cloth which accompanies the solution. If untarnished but dulled, just clean as for gold jewellery.

Gold jewellery. This needs a wash in warm, soapy water, drying in a soft cloth and polishing with a chamois leather.

Emeralds. These should be cared for as diamonds and other gemstones, but extra care should be taken because they can chip or become scratched if knocked against another hard surface.

Enamelled jewellery. This should be cleaned by dipping in a mild solution of pure soapsuds and hot water to which a few drops of ammonia have been added. Polish off with a very soft cloth.

Lapis Lazuli. Same as coral.

Marcasite should not be washed. All that is needed is to rub it with a soft brush and finish off with a gentle polishing with a chamois leather.

Mother of Pearl. A lightweight oil should be sparingly applied with a soft cloth, finishing off with a soft clean cloth for the final polishing.

Opals. You are recommended to take these to a jeweller for treatment.

Turquoise. Same as opals. These are absorbent jewels, so keep away from grease.

13

BE CHARMING

Charm to a woman is like cream on a cake, delectable if fresh and natural and used with discretion, sickly and overpowering in excess. It should be as natural as breathing. It knows no age barriers and beguiles as no other feminine quality.

Artificial charm is a sin against femininity and it cloys like over-sweetened tea.

In its natural form, charm will make a plain or ugly woman attractive, and it adds warmth to the character of a beautiful woman.

Miss Bardot has it; Ginette Spanier, Balmain's directrice, has it; Dame Sybil Thorndike has it; Irene Handl has it and so has actress Romy Schneider, model Jean Shrimpton, broadcaster Jean Metcalfe and beautician Helena Rubinstein.

Charm is the way you are, the way you talk, the way you think, act and move. It is a thousand and one mysterious and different things. You will become more charming if you study the following do's and don'ts of charm, then forget the fact that you did so. Let them bubble in your background, never force charm. Above all things it should be spontaneous.

Do be considerate towards others.

DON'T pretend to be helpless and scatty if you're not.

Do be a good listener. Never look bored, even if you feel that way.

DON'T wear jangly bracelets at work.

Do wear a perfume that suits your personality.

DON'T leave lipstick traces on cups.

Do be honest, but learn to be tactful at the same time.

DON'T smoke in the street.

Do be punctual for appointments.

DON'T wear heavy make-up. It cheapens your appearance.

Do learn to use your eyes, especially when you smile.

DON'T overdrink alcohol at any time. Take a glass of tonic water with a slice of lemon when you have had your "safe" quota. It looks like a gin and tonic anyway!

Do take a small gift such as a plant, packet of cigarettes or a handkerchief, for your hostess when invited to her home for dinner. Give it to her unobtrusively.

DON'T be afraid to say that you don't understand if someone starts to talk "over your head." Much better to do this than risk making a fool of yourself by saying the wrong thing.

Do learn to accept a compliment graciously and with thanks.

DON'T fidget at the cinema or theatre.

Do learn to be quietly appreciative of efforts by a host or hostess at a social event.

DON'T wear deeply plunging necklines when the man in your life is taking you to a business dinner. Be discreet and leave a little to the imagination!

Do cultivate a warm sense of humour.

DON'T be over-demonstrative in public.

Do remember the importance of unexpected kindnesses to other people.

DON'T raise your voice in public.

Do try to be broadminded and tolerant.

DON'T be rough or vulgar.

Do be subtle, loyal and gentle.

DON'T be cynical.

Do be ready to let someone else have the last say in an

argument once in a while. You'll be liked all the more for it.

And finally DO be yourself. Don't copy other people.

Cary Grant sees charm in naturalness. Jack Hedley, the man who won thousands of feminine hearts when he played detective Tim Frazer on television, told me over lunch one day: "To me it's the fresh look. Gingham frocks and the smell of soap. Women in smart hats frighten the life out of me!" To singer Yves Montand, charm is a woman being a woman.

American businessman, Charles Revson, the spruce president of the world's largest retail cosmetic organisation, gave me these thoughts on charm: "Never, with women, can you take anything for granted, every woman always has some unknown quantity. She is always changing, that is her never-ending attraction. She is always creating mysteries about herself; her clothes, and fashions change, she changes her make-up, she changes mentally and emotionally. By aiming for real beauty potential, she can actually affect herself spiritually.

"She has the right to be conservative, and the right to be daring. All this is part and parcel of feminine charm."

Popular television personality, Cliff Michelmore, cleverly draws a dividing line between a woman who is charming and a woman who is merely a charmer.

He says: "Charm is a secret gift nearly every woman wishes she had, but only a few possess. To me, it has nothing to do with the senses or the way she dresses or walks or talks. The charming woman has an invisible light inside her which shines through everything she does.

"But the charmer frightens me, and I find myself repelled rather than attracted. The charmer knows she is being charming, the charming woman is usually unconscious of her gift."

112

Charm and the Awkward Situation

Here are some awkward and embarrassing situations which could happen to anyone. The secret is to retain your poise whenever you are stumped or startled.

A waiter drops soup on your dress during dinner. Keep calm at all costs! And smile. Say that it was obviously an accident, and, if necessary, excuse yourself quietly and go for a quick sponge in the powder-room. Never make a loud fuss in public. If your gown needs cleaning it may be in your interests to see the manager afterwards to check on appropriate compensation.

You are having dinner in an exclusive restaurant, and the waiter brings you an all-French menu which you cannot understand. Be frank and honest in a cheerful way and tell your escort. Ask him to choose for you. If he can't understand French or you are alone, the waiter will help you.

While having dinner at a friend's house you find a small caterpillar in the lettuce heart, which has somehow missed being washed out. Above all, don't make a fuss! Don't say anything in fact, as it could cause your hostess great embarrassment. Push the unsuspecting offender under the leaf and hope that it doesn't re-appear.

You appear at a function wearing a hat you were told was an exclusive model, only to find someone else is wearing an identical style. Do not, whatever happens, look daggers drawn at the person wearing the hat. It isn't her fault. The best thing is to have a smile over it if your eyes meet. The time for plain-speaking is later, when you return to the milliner!

You are about to introduce a friend to someone and suddenly realise that you cannot remember that someone's name. Honesty is the best policy. Smile and apologise sincerely, saying: "I'm so sorry but your name has just slipped my mind." Try and prevent a similar occurrence by repeating to yourself the names of people who are introduced to you, before you leave them.

At an important social function you are given a strange dish which you have no idea how to tackle. In this instance think and act s-l-o-w. Continue talking with your neighbour, or take a moment longer with your wine, until you see how other people tackle it.

You are entertaining a guest to lunch in a restaurant or hotel, and the hot meal you ordered turns out to be cold or badly presented. You will want to complain, and rightly so, but there is an art in doing this. Do not complain so loudly that people at adjoining tables turn around to see what is happening. Call the head waiter and explain your complaint quietly. This is far more effective, and lessens any possible embarrassment to your guest.

You are staying with someone and you accidentally break an ornament. Be genuinely sincere in your apology and offer to make good the breakage if at all possible, otherwise offer to have it repaired.

14

THE SOUND OF BEAUTY

A warm, modulated and expressive voice sets the final seal on a woman's beauty. It may be likened to a lovely countryside with undulating hills and variety around every corner. Remove the colour and character and you are left with a monotonous sound, boring as an unrelieved plain.

In order to improve your voice you must first of all hear it. A tape recorder is the best way, but failing this try cupping a hand behind each ear, bringing them round a little at the side, and then talking. It is also a good idea to ask a close friend or member of the family to tell you honestly whether your voice sounds good or bad, alive or lazy. They can also point out any speech patterns that you may have.

Some people, for example, have a habit of saying "You see," "You know" or "Understand?" at the end of every other sentence. Patterns such as this may be removed with a little forethought and concentration.

To speak well, you must be relaxed, and in order to be relaxed you must breathe well and naturally. Practise by breathing in deeply through your nostrils and right into the lungs. Hold your breath and count five to yourself, then let your breath out slowly and evenly through your mouth. Do this three or four times taking care not to force your breath in any way. Now take in your breath again, and this time when you release it say "Ah-h-h-h-h" until it has all been dispelled.

When you speak, aim at a medium to low pitched voice

which comes from the base of your diaphragm, not merely from your throat. This way your voice gains in depth and quality and loses any harsh thinness it may have. If you speak correctly you should be able to feel a slight movement around the area of your diaphragm, which you can feel by resting the palm of your hand on your midriff beneath your bosom.

When you have a few minutes to spare on your own, run through the vowel sounds A E I O U and then the remainder of the alphabet. *Use* your lips, teeth and tongue, watching yourself in a mirror to make sure that your mouth is really working.

The English language has a vast and exciting vocabulary, but many people do not use it to advantage because they talk in mono-syllabic grunts with slurred and lazy speech. "Gonna" instead of "going to," and "lil' " instead of "little," are two typical examples.

Even perfect speech is nothing without expression, and this also can be really improved with a few solo sessions before the bedroom or bathroom mirror.

Pretend you are an actress for a moment and attempt to convey, via your facial expression, the emotions of happiness, horror, anger, disgust, enthusiasm, sympathy, sadness, kindness, joy, tragedy and any others you may think of, and see for yourself how alive your face can be.

Ways to Improve your Speech

1. Learn first of all to be a good listener! Listen to the voices of accomplished narrators and personalities on the radio and television, hear the intonations of their voices and watch their facial expressions. Listen to your friends talking so that you can answer intelligently.

2. Read aloud for a few minutes each day. If possible, choose an old or new classic. The essays of G. K. Chesterton and Charles Lamb make fascinating reading. This

way you not only expand your vocabulary but get used to hearing your voice.

3. The day of the dumb blonde has passed! Make sure that you have something to say by broadening your interests, particularly if you are a housewife and probably confined to the home for much of the day. Read as much as possible. Take a correspondence course. Join a club or society for the arts, handicrafts or debate or take part in a voluntary welfare organisation. If you already have a particular interest, gardening perhaps, read and learn as much as you can about all its aspects; the history of gardens, famous gardeners, etc.

4. Watch your grammar. It is surprising how many people will say: "They was at the pictures," or "We was in the garden." "Was" should never be used after the plural "we" or "they", only after the first and third person singular, i.e. I was, or he, she or it was.

5. Pronounce your words, don't run them into each other. Say "How do you do," rather than "Howjado" and "lots of" instead of "lotsa."

6. Don't mumble. Practise saying: "Betty bought some yellow butter at the baker's shop" and let each word ring clear.

7. Be concise and compact. The quickest way to lose the attention of others is to ramble on and take half an hour to tell a five minute story. Make sure that your words mean something, like the gestures of an actor on the stage.

8. Give yourself more confidence by speaking in public, even if it is only to ask a question at a meeting. Stand up, relax, and speak briskly, neither too fast nor too slow.

9. Another way to hold a person's attention is to look at them between the eyes.

10. Put texture into your voice when necessary. When

you say "rough" think of a coarse blanket or a stone wall. Say "smooth" and think of c-r-e-a-m.

11. Bring your powers of observation and description to play in conversation, so that people will enjoy hearing you talk about the most ordinary things. It would be far more interesting to say "There were plump, well-sprung sparrows on the lawn this morning" rather than "There were sparrows on the lawn this morning."

12. Always be sincere and genuine in whatever you say. An affected, artificial accent such as "dahling" or "aictually" will immediately put people on their guard.

The Telephone

Never underestimate the power of a telephone. It is a transmitter of personality and character *par excellence*. When you answer a phone give your name and number clearly and distinctly, and when phoning anyone always give your name in the first instance to avoid confusion.

If you work in an office be friendly, but business-like, and always helpful. An abrupt "'allo" will not endear you or your firm to the caller. Think "bright" and convey the pleasure of a smile through the warmth of your voice, and never talk on the phone with a cigarette or sweet in your mouth.

Communication

Finally, don't take your voice and speech for granted. Together with the written word, it provides a means of communication that is second to none in the world.

Take full advantage of it and you will find new confidence in yourself.

15

BEAUTY CASEBOOK

Why are some women more attractive than others? What is it that enables a girl to rise from poverty in Italy to become a world famous beauty, although her statistics are far from perfect? Why will one girl win nearly every beauty contest heat that she enters and leave other contestants standing? What is it that makes a man or a woman look twice, and then again at a woman?

Sophia Loren has large hips, a wide melon-slice of a mouth and extra height, but she is beautiful. Why? Because she is supremely happy to be herself. Instead of letting extra inches get the better of her, she makes the most of them with a display of statuesque grace, and she uses her over-generous mouth to give wonderful smiles.

Princess Alexandra, now the Hon. Mrs. Angus Ogilvie, is tall and she isn't blessed with the neatest of noses, but everyone remarks on her beauty. Why? I have studied her at close quarters and seen a girl who is proud of her inches, carries herself well without stooping and wears absolutely simple clothes, often off the peg, that make her height and full figure an asset. Long ago she dismissed the starchiness of British Royalty and she will talk spontaneously to anyone wives and pose for delighted photographers.

Jean Shrimpton, the young English model who has appeared on countless glossy magazine covers throughout the world, is on the lanky side, with a face that *could* be plain. But her face is in constant demand. Why? Her secret is complete adaptability to mood and atmosphere.

She can be a sweet young thing, an aloof aristocrat, an infectiously gay personality or just plain tender. Her make-up is always natural and she retains one of the essences of womanly beauty, a sense of mystery.

I have seen Caroline Wedgwood Benn, wife of the Labour M.P. and a busy mother into the bargain, looking attractive in the midst of a rush and life that would leave many a woman wilting. Exuberance is her strong point, coupled with thick lovely hair, which she wears softly framing her face, and perfect legs, which she arranges to elegant advantage whenever she sits down.

I have watched and judged beauty contests where there have been a handful of statistically perfect girls. The final choice always has an extra quality known as "life."

If you study the majority of so-called beautiful or attractive women or girls, you will find that they all have this inner spark of vitality, together with enthusiasm for everything that goes on around them, and a genuine interest in people, places and things.

They are never afraid to show their keenness either. Barbara Goalen, the forerunner of all the top post-war models, once attended an elegant cocktail party after attending the opening of a dress salon in Liverpool. Somehow, at first glance, one expected her to be as aloof as a prize cat, and then she voiced an enthusiastic wish to have a really good look at the docks! She was natural and unassuming, as are all true beauties.

Blueprints for Beauty

Lady Isobel Barnett, a television personality, and Lady Mavis Pilkington, wife of industrialist Sir Harry Pilkington, are often in the public eye, and both are good examples of women who know their faults and assets and have generally come to terms with them.

Both are frank about their problems. "I have naturally

wavy hair," said Lady Barnett, "and my difficulty is trying to keep it smooth, now that waves are unfashionable."

Said Lady Pilkington: "My bosom seems to be my worst feature, as I am heavily built. However, as I have had it since I was fourteen I have learned to live with it and take great care over choosing good boned bras and flattering bodices and necklines."

Let these two attractive busy women give their individual answers to ten beauty questions.

What gives you the biggest uplift in the shortest time?

Lady Barnett: A delicious lasting perfume, so that I can sniff myself occasionally and enjoy it.

Lady Pilkington: Eye make-up with a brown eyeliner and pencil, and turquoise blue shadow blended with a little brown to give a deep identifiable colour.

What is the most valuable tip you have learned about make-up?

Lady Barnett: To put on one layer of lipstick, blot it, and wait two minutes before applying a second coat. Blot again. The colour stays on for hours.

Lady Pilkington: I have two really. One, the blending of blue and brown eye shadow, was passed on to me by Catherine Boyle, and the other, which I learned early in life, was never to overdo make-up and to apply it with skill.

Could you give details of your make-up routine?

Lady Barnett: I make up fully first thing in the morning as I cannot face the day without my "face," and I always try to have a second fresh make-up during the day, and again in the evening. I have a dry skin, so I use a moisture base, a tinted foundation and powder. I use a thick nourishing cream when I have my bath and let it soak in, and use a moisture liquid at night. Occasionally I have a salon facial when I have time and my skin looks jaded.

Lady Pilkington: I find that using small cleansing pads to remove make-up at night keeps my skin in good condition and I never seem to need a facial in a salon. My skin is inclined to be oily in parts, so it does not dry or wrinkle, and as a result I can wash my face in soap and water without harm, although I do follow with a moisturising skin freshener. I always use an eyebath with cold water and some eyedrops. I start my make-up with a liquid base on the face and neck, and use a pancake make-up on my nose which is oily. Following eye make-up I touch up with a cake powder (never have used loose) and finally a pinky flame lipstick which I blot with tissue. This all takes about 20 minutes, but apart from refreshing the foundation and lipstick once in the day with another cleansing pad, that is all I do.

Do you like to emphasise any particular quality?

Lady Barnett: I take especial care with my eyes, using shadow and a line above the lashes.

Lady Pilkington: My husband says my eyes are my best feature, but I think my teeth and nails are. My nails are long and strong fortunately and I keep them well varnished. If possible I try and clean my teeth five times a day!

Do you have a daily exercise routine?

Lady Barnett: No routine as such, but I play golf and tennis and swim and ride instead.

Lady Pilkington: Tennis in the summer and sometimes on indoor courts in the winter, plus long walks and three strenuous sets of table tennis almost every morning before my husband leaves for work. I love dancing, and given a moment's chance I really enjoy a Twist and a high kick in the bedroom with the radio!

What does good grooming mean to you?

Lady Barnett: Scrupulous cleanliness and neatness. Cleanliness is easy, but neatness takes time and forethought so that clothes, gloves, etc. are cleaned and pressed when needed.

Lady Pilkington: Cleanliness above all. Clothes must be clean and well pressed, bags and shoes neat and clean. A weekly visit to the hairdresser is an essential, and a good hair spray is invaluable as long as it is brushed out daily. Many women slip up at the end of a careful toilet by forgetting to brush away any stray hairs on their clothes. A beautiful outfit can be ruined this way.

What mental qualities do you feel are essential to inner beauty?

Lady Barnett: Tranquillity and a sense of humour. You will get lines on your face if you can laugh at life and at yourself sometimes, but at least they will be the right lines!

Lady Pilkington: A lively mind, being interested in everybody and everything, a kind sympathetic nature and self-confidence.

The Proof

In case anyone should doubt the beauty bonuses resultant from exercise, meet Molly Palmer who has walked over 24,800 miles in the last 16 years, has perfect natural colouring and a complexion as clear as that of any famous film star.

Miss Palmer, five feet three inches in height, dark and vivacious, is a post woman who rises at 5.15 every morning and walks five miles on and around a slice of South Wales coast.

In the beauty stakes she is an example to any woman. The wettest windiest day will always see her immaculate both in dress and make-up. She made no secret of her simple, common-sense routine: "I really believe that an iron is one of a woman's best friends when it comes to grooming, and I press my clothes and uniform regularly. I wear a clean shirt and fresh undies daily, use a light make-up and keep a compact tucked in a pocket of my post bag, where it is handy for quick touch-ups."

Miss Palmer is a great believer in perfume as a "signature mark", and has discovered that a sense of humour, patience and calmness, make day-to-day life pleasurable rather than a bore.

Her long walks in all weathers, six days a week, have given her an immunity from colds (there's an incentive to walk to the next bus stop in the mornings, if ever there was one!) and she looks upon early rising not as a hardship but as something really to be enjoyed. Every day in the early hours she looks for something to stimulate her mind, whether it is the seasonal change of a tree or the pattern of rain on the road.

In this way she has become genuinely happy in her work, and, perhaps more important, an attractive woman by virtue of her full interest in life.

And therein lies a beauty moral for all of us.

Index

The asterisked page numbers* refer to illustrations

125